The Story of the Horse Family in the Modern World and through Sixty Million Years of History

New York

OXFORD UNIVERSITY PRESS

1951

HORSES

HORSES

George Gaylord Simpson

To my Mother and to the memory of my Father

PREFACE

WHEN the late Henry Fairfield Osborn established a Department of Mammalian Paleontology at The American Museum of Natural History in 1891, one of his chief aims was to assemble a large collection of horses, recent and fossil, and to compile everything known about this fascinating group of animals. An ultimate result was to be publication of 'a full history of the horse from the earliest times to the present.'

During Professor Osborn's lifetime (which ended in 1935) a tremendous amount of material was accumulated on the history of the horse, and this work still continues. A roster of all the workers concerned in earlier collecting, preparation, and study would be too long for the present pages, but a few names must not be omitted. Among those who both collected fossil horses and made technical studies of them were W. D. Matthew, J. W. Gidley, and Walter Granger. Preparation and mounting of skeletons were at first under the direction of Adam Hermann, later of Albert Thomson, who was also a collector of note, and of Charles Lang. S. H. Chubb devoted the greater part of his lifetime to preparation of skeletons of recent horses as another aspect of this program. Support came from many sources, among which the benefactions of William C. Whitney deserve special mention.

Under Osborn, a large staff of secretaries, librarians, artists, and research assistants also worked on the horse program, amassing a great stack of portfolios of notes and illustrations and many drawers of index cards. Most of the fossil finds were described in technical papers. Besides many shorter papers, in 1918 most of the American Museum fossil horses except the earliest and the latest were described

in a highly technical, large quarto memoir by Osborn. At the other
extreme, a popular booklet, *Evolution of the Horse,* by Matthew
and Chubb, was issued in 1913. This interested and instructed generations of students and museum visitors. It was so popular and so
sound that it was kept in print without essential change for many
years.

With all this labor and in spite of voluminous publications on
special aspects of the subject, the 'full history of the horse' for which
Osborn started preparations and carried them so far was never written. Even in Osborn's lifetime, the materials outgrew any possibility
of handling them as he originally planned. With the scale and scope
envisioned by him, the treatise would have become a monumental
work of many volumes and could not possibly have been written by
one man or in one lifetime.

The present book is an effort finally to carry out the departmental
plan of sixty years' standing, but to do so on a scale incomparably
more modest than was anticipated by Osborn and his staff. This
book is, indeed, intended to be a 'full history of the horse,' as far as
such a history can now be written, but it is a history in broad outline only, with most of the technical details rigorously suppressed.
The book is also intended to be in a sense a successor to Matthew
and Chubb's fine work, considerably expanded in scope and brought
down to date. It was decided further to include here not only a
sufficient non-technical account of the horse family, ancient and recent, but also various aspects of zoology, geology, and principles of
evolution with the horses as an example. Those interested primarily
in horses may thus see these animals in the broader framework of
time and life into which they fit. Those mainly interested in more
general subjects and principles may use the book to supply the sense
of reality and the check on theory best provided by a concrete
example.

The present book draws on the whole mass of specimens and data
accumulated by all my predecessors in the American Museum.
Acknowledgments are gratefully made to the memories of Osborn,
Matthew, Granger, Gidley, Thomson, and all the many others who
labored with them. Among current associates in the Department of

Geology and Paleontology, all concerned with fossil vertebrates have in various ways encouraged and assisted me. Special mention is due Mrs. Rachel H. Nichols for assistance in connection with the departmental library, catalogue, and files of illustrations and notes in her care. Although not specifically concerned with this project, my colleagues Drs. E. H. Colbert and B. Schaeffer have indirectly promoted it in various ways. Most of our present laboratory and field force, consisting of Carl Sorensen, G. O. Whitaker, W. E. Fish, and Walter Sorensen, have at some time been concerned with collecting and preparing fossil horses. Secretarial and related assistance was by Louis A. Monaco and Gloria Wagner.

During the preparation of this book, its substance was used as basis for a one-semester course given at the American Museum for Columbia University, with Edward Hawkins as classroom assistant. A stimulating group of students considerably clarified the organization of horse history.

Credits for illustrations and technical data additional to the information in the captions are given in the list of plates, p. xiii, and figures, p. xvii. In addition to detailed acknowledgments of sources, this list should be consulted for such facts as the names and owners of living domestic horses shown in the plates or the full technical names and museum numbers of the illustrated fossil skeletons. For the compilation and preparation of illustrations, general acknowledgments and thanks are due to the Department of Education and the Staff Illustrators Corps of The American Museum of Natural History. Dr. W. G. Doyle, in charge of popular publications, spent much time on the task of locating suitable materials and assisted in other ways, as did R. I. Garton. The numerous new drawings and preparation of all text figures were carried out by T. W. Voter, supervisor of the staff corps, and by Paula Hutchison, Walter Holmquist, and Alexander Seidel, staff artists.

Outside of the American Museum, information on breeds and related data have been supplied by the following:

The Horse and Mule Association of America, Wayne Dinsmore, Sec.; Welsh Pony Society of America, Frank H. Smith, Sec., and Charles K. Bassett; The Arabian Horse Club of America, Frank Watt, Sec.; The Jockey Club, W. D. Daingerfield; American Saddle Horse Breeders Association, C. J. Cronan, Jr., Sec.; Percheron Horse Association of America, Ellis McFarland, Sec.; American Shire Horse Association, E. F. Fox, Sec.; The Morgan Horse Club, F. B. Hills, Sec.; Tennessee Walking Horse Breeders' Association, Syd Houston, Sec., and G. M. Orr, in charge of publicity; The American Quarter Horse Association, Raymond D. Hollingsworth, Sec.; Cleveland Bay Society of America, A. Mackay-Smith, Sec.; Belgian Draft Horse Corporation of America, H. J. Brant, Sec.; The American Albino Horse Club, Ruth Thompson, Sec.; The Pinto Horse Society, G. M. Glendenning, Sec.; Palomino Horse Breeders of America, H. A. Zappe, Sec.; The Palomino Horse Association, J. M. Fagan, Sec.; Appaloosa Horse Club, G. B. Hatley, Sec.; The American Suffolk Horse Association, L. B. Westcott, Sec.; Armour's Livestock Bureau, E. N. Wentworth, Director; Calumet Farm, Margaret Glass, Sec.

Information on collections of fossil horses was received from the following:

Museum of Comparative Zoology, Harvard University, A. S. Romer; Peabody Museum of Natural History, Yale University, J. T. Gregory; Princeton University, G. L. Jepsen; The Academy of Natural Sciences of Philadelphia, B. F. Howell, and M. D. Reed; Carnegie Museum, J. LeR. Kay; U.S. National Museum, C. L. Gazin; University of Michigan, C. W. Hibbard; Chicago Natural History Museum, B. Patterson; University of Chicago, E. C. Olson; University of Kansas, R. R. Camp; University of Nebraska, C. B. Schultz; South Dakota School of Mines and Technology, J. D. Bump; The Colorado Museum of Natural History, A. M. Bailey; Amherst College, A. E. Wood; University of Wyoming, P. O. McGrew; University of California, R. A. Stirton; Los Angeles County Museum, H. Howard; California Institute of Technology, C. Stock.

George E. Nitzsche, Philadelphia, assisted in obtaining information on Muybridge.

The index has been prepared by David B. Kitts.

I wish also to thank the staff of Oxford University Press for their care and skill in editing and designing this volume.

So many individuals and organizations have helped in some way that a few may have been inadvertently omitted in the preceding acknowledgments. If so, apologies are extended. I should also add the customary caution that I alone am responsible for all opinions and all errors in this book.

G. G. S.

New York
10 *November* 1950

CONTENTS

Plates, xiii

Text Figures, xvii

Introduction, xxi

Part One: LIVING HORSES

1. What Is a Horse?, 3

2. A Look at *Equus,* 7

3. The Living Wild Equidae, 17

4. Horses and History, 24

5. Ancient Breeds, 34

6. Some European Breeds in America, 42

7. An Interlude on Gaits and the Invention of Motion Pictures, 52

8. American Breeds and Their Forerunners, 59

9. A Horse of Another Color, 69

Part Two: THE LINEAGE OF THE HORSE

10. Hunters and Hunting of Fossil Horses, 85

11. Time-scale of Horse History, 98

12. Forerunners of the Horses, 103

13. The Little Eohippus, 113

14. Other Eocene Horses, 120

15. Early Three-toed Horses, 124

16. The Great Transformation, 131

17. Later Three-toed Horses, 137

18. One-toed Horses, 142

19. The Horse's Relatives, 151

20. False Horses, 158

Part Three: HORSES AND EVOLUTION

21. Evidence in Court, 163

22. How Horses Changed: Skull and Brain, 172

23. How Horses Changed: Teeth, 181

24. How Horses Changed: Limbs and Feet, 190

25. Patterns of Evolution, 205

26. Explanations of Evolution, 218

Appendices

  A. Where to See Fossil Horses, 227

  B. Where to Read More about Horses, 232

Index, 237

PLATES

(Credits and data additional to those in the captions are given here. A.M.N.H. = The American Museum of Natural History. I.C. = Illustrators Corps. The author is responsible for scientific planning and data in illustrations by I.C.)

I. Domestic horse with points labeled. New labeling by A.M.N.H., I.C., on photograph of Jubilee Gold, a registered Morgan (AMH 8430) and palomino (PHBA 6591), Don Nicholson, owner. Photograph by Stover Studio, Oakland

II. Skeleton of a domestic horse. New labeling by I.C. on A.M.N.H. photograph of a trotting horse skeleton mounted by S. H. Chubb in A.M.N.H.

III. Teeth and incisor age series of domestic horses. A.M.N.H. photographs of preparations by S. H. Chubb in A.M.N.H.

IV. Some living wild equids. (a) *Equus caballus prjewalskii*, photograph from New York Zoological Society. (b) *Equus hemionus*, Mongolian race, photograph by A.M.N.H. (c) *Equus asinus*, photograph from New York Zoological Society

V. Zebras. (a) *Equus quagga granti*, A.M.N.H. photograph of mounted specimen in A.M.N.H. (b) *Equus quagga quagga*, photograph from Zoological Society of London. (c) *Equus zebra*, painting by C. R. Knight, A.M.N.H. (d) *Equus grevyi*, photograph from New York Zoological Society

VI. Horses in ancient art. (a) Stone Age painting in Cave of Altamira, after Breuil and Obermaier. (b) Assyrian relief, photograph from the Metropolitan Museum of Art. (c) Greek relief, photograph from the Metropolitan Museum of Art. (d) Greek statuette, photograph from the Metropolitan Museum of Art

VII. Two old types of horses. (a) Arabs on desert horses, painting by A. Schreyer, from the Metropolitan Museum of Art. (b) modern Arabian, Cassim (2556), photograph by J. F. Abernathy from the owner, Dr. George Conn. (c) an Iceland pony, photograph from A.M.N.H. files

VIII. Old European types of horses. (a) light cavalry horse, print by
Vernet from *Dessins de Chevau,* vol. xx. (b) medieval Great Horse,
print by Dürer, from the Metropolitan Museum of Art

IX. Some breeds of European origin. (a) Percheron, Enchanter, (212346),
Fred Gwinn, owner, photograph from Percheron Horse Association of
America. (b) Belgian, Betty (28290), W. G. Harkness and son, owners,
photograph by Harley Hoffman, Castalia, Ohio. (c) Clydesdale, Archer,
photograph by J. F. Abernathy. (d) Suffolk, imported stallion, photograph by Strohmeyer and Carpenter from the American Suffolk Horse
Association

X. Some breeds of European origin. (a) Cleveland Bay, Orion, imported
stallion, photograph from A. Mackay Smith, White Post, Virginia. (b)
Hackney, Cassilis Reveler, photograph by H. Haas from the owner,
Mrs. J. Macy Willets. (c) Welsh Pony, Coed Coch Gwinc (8965), imported mare, photograph from the owner, Charles K. Bassett. (d)
Thoroughbred, Citation, Calumet Farm, painting copyright by Men-
asco, reproduced by permission

XI. (a) Eadweard Muybridge, oil portrait by Elsa Koenig Nitzsche in
the library of the University of Pennsylvania. (b) Muybridge's track
and cameras, photograph by Muybridge, from Stanford University.
(c) artist's wrong conception of the gallop, print by Alken, 1820, from
the Spencer Collection, New York Public Library. (d) horse galloping,
from Muybridge's *Animals in Motion*

XII. American breeds of horses. (a) Standard Bred trotting horse, Rod-
ney, photograph from U.S. Trotting Association. (b) Morgan, Abbott
(7704), photograph by Strohmeyer and Carpenter, from the Morgan
Horse Club. (c) Quarter Horse, Hired Hand, photograph by Neal
Lyons, from the American Quarter Horse Association. (d) American
Saddle Horse, Spring Cheer, Mrs. William Taylor, owner, up, photo-
graph by Carl Klein. (e) Tennessee Walking Horse, Merry Go Boy,
W. Wiser, E. Mallard, and R. W. Norman, owners, photograph from
Winston Wiser, Shelbyville, Tennessee

XIII. Color patterns in horses. (a) Palomino, Jubilee Gold, Don Nicholson, owner, photograph from Stover Studio, Oakland. (b) Pinto, Hi-
dalgo (PHS 272), George M. Glendenning, owner, up, photograph
from Pinto Horse Society. (c) Appaloosa, Toby (AHC 113), George B.
Hatley, owner, photograph from the Appaloosa Horse Club. (d) 'Albino,' White Wings (AAHC 320), Cal Thompson, owner, up, photograph from the American Albino Horse Club

XIV. (a) Owen's *Hyracotherium* skull, after Owen. (b) V. Kovalevsky,
from Dollo. (c) T. H. Huxley, A.M.N.H. files. (d) Joseph Leidy,
A.M.N.H. files

XV. Students of fossil horses. (a) O. C. Marsh, A.M.N.H. files. (b) E. D. Cope, A.M.N.H. files. (c) H. F. Osborn, A.M.N.H. files.

XVI. Students of fossil horses and of evolution. (a) W. D. Matthew, A.M.N.H. files. (b) W. B. Scott, A.M.N.H. files. (c) Charles Darwin, A.M.N.H. files

XVII. Collecting fossil horses. (a) quarry diagram, A.M.N.H. (b) collecting party, A.M.N.H.

XVIII. Collecting and mounting fossil horses. (a) skeleton of *Hypohippus* in the rock, A.M.N.H. (b) finishing mount of eohippus, A.M.N.H.

XIX. *Phenacodus*. (a) skeleton, *Phenacodus primaevus,* from the lower Eocene of the Bighorn Basin, Wyoming, A.M.N.H. No. 4369. (b) restoration by Charles R. Knight for A.M.N.H.

XX. Eohippus (=*Hyracotherium*). (a) skeleton, *Hyracotherium venticolum,* type, lower Eocene of Wind River Basin, Wyoming, A.M.N.H. No. 4832, A.M.N.H. photograph. (b) restoration by Charles R. Knight for A.M.N.H.

XXI. Fossil horse skeletons. (a) *Orohippus osbornianus,* middle Eocene of Bridger Basin, Wyoming, A.M.N.H. No. 12648, A.M.N.H. photograph. (b) *Miohippus intermedius,* type, upper Oligocene of the Big Badlands, South Dakota, A.M.N.H. No. 1196, A.M.N.H. photograph

XXII. *Mesohippus*. (a) skeleton, *Mesohippus bairdii,* from the middle Oligocene of the Big Badlands, South Dakota, A.M.N.H. No. 1477, A.M.N.H. photograph. (b) restoration by Charles R. Knight for A.M.N.H.

XXIII. *Hypohippus*. (a) skeleton, *Hypohippus osborni,* from the Miocene of Pawnee Creek, Colorado, A.M.N.H. No. 9407, A.M.N.H. photograph. (b) restoration by Charles R. Knight for A.M.N.H.

XXIV. *Merychippus*. (a) skeleton, *Merychippus isonesus quintus,* type, from the Miocene of Sheep Creek, Nebraska, A.M.N.H. No. 14185, A.M.N.H. photograph. (b) restoration by A.M.N.H., I.C.

XXV. *Neohipparion*. (a) skeleton, *Neohipparion whitneyi,* type, from the early Pliocene of Little White River, South Dakota, A.M.N.H. No. 9815, A.M.N.H. photograph. (b) restoration by Charles R. Knight for A.M.N.H.

XXVI. *Pliohippus*. (a) skeleton, *Pliohippus leidyanus,* type, from the Pliocene of Snake Creek, Nebraska, A.M.N.H. No. 17224, A.M.N.H. photograph. (b) restoration by John C. Germann for A.M.N.H.

XXVII. *Equus (Plesippus)*. (a) skeleton, *Equus (Plesippus) simplicidens,* from the Blancan (late Pliocene or early Pleistocene) of Blanco Canyon,

Texas, A.M.N.H. No. 20076 (skull cast from 20077), A.M.N.H. photograph. (b) restoration by Charles R. Knight for A.M.N.H.

XXVIII. *Equus (Equus)*. (a) skeleton, *Equus scotti,* type, Pleistocene of Rock Creek, Texas, A.M.N.H. No. 10606, A.M.N.H. photograph. (b) restoration by Charles R. Knight for A.M.N.H.

XXIX. *Hippidion.* (a) skeleton, *Hippidion bonaerense,* from the Pleistocene of the Rio Luján, Argentina, A.M.N.H. No. 11872, mount of cast from the Museo de La Plata, Argentina, A.M.N.H. photograph. (b) restoration by A.M.N.H., I.C.

XXX. Extinct relatives of the horse. (a) *Brontotherium,* restoration by Charles R. Knight for A.M.N.H. (b) *Moropus,* restoration by E. S. Christman for A.M.N.H.

XXXI. Living relatives of the horse. (a) *Tapirus terrestris,* photograph from New York Zoological Society. (b) *Dicerus bicornis,* A.M.N.H. photograph of mounted specimens in A.M.N.H.

XXXII. (a) *Diadiaphorus,* restoration by Charles R. Knight for W. B. Scott, Princeton University. (b) galloping eohippus and *Equus* skeletons, after H. F. Osborn, whose figure incorporated material from Muybridge

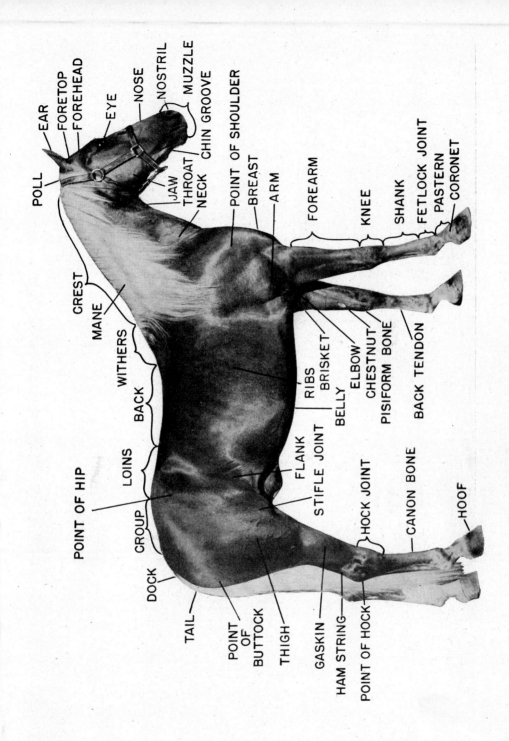

A horse with parts, or points, labeled.

I

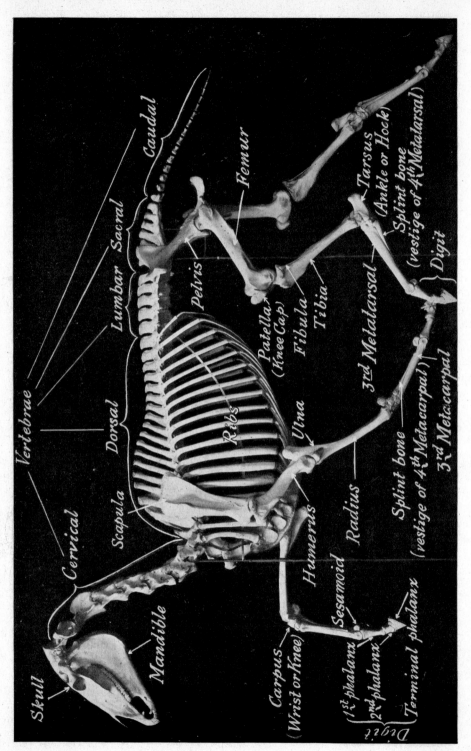

Horse skeleton, with principal bones labeled.

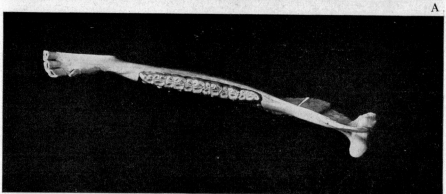

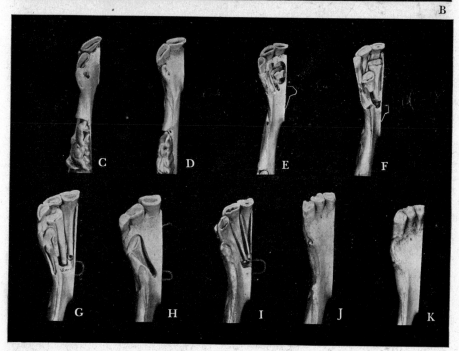

The teeth of the domestic horse. (a) Left half of skull, seen from below, with all teeth in place. (b) Left half of lower jaw, seen from above, with all teeth in place. (c-k) Front ends of left sides of lower jaws, to show age characters of incisor teeth. Ages as follows: (c) 2 days; (d) 4-6 weeks; (e) 11 months; (f) 2 years; (g) 3½ years; (h) 4 years; (i) 5 years; (j) 17 years; (k) 39 years.

III

A

B

C

Some living wild equids. (a) Przewalski's horse, *Equus prjewalskii,* of central Asia. (b) So-called wild ass of Mongolia, *Equus hemionus.* (c) True wild ass of Africa, *Equus asinus.*

IV

Zebras. (a) Grant's zebra, *Equus quagga granti*, one of the numerous kinds of bonte-quaggas. (b) The extinct quagga, *Equus quagga quagga*. (c) Mountain zebra, *Equus zebra*. (d) Grévy's zebra, *Equus grévyi*.

V

C

D

A

B

Horses in ancient art. (a) Old Stone Age painting on the wall of the Cave of Altamira, Spain. (b) Assyrian warrior leading two horses (probably chariot horses). (c) Classical Greek relief of bareback rider and horse. (d) Classical Greek bronze statuette of horse.

B

C

A

Two old types of horses. (a) Arabs on desert horses. (b) Modern Arabian. (c) Iceland Pony, a modern representative of the ancient Celtic type.

VII

A

B

Old European types of horses. (a) Light riding horse—a light cavalry horse. (b) Heavy horse—the medieval Great Horse.

VIII

A

B

C

D

Some breeds of European origin. (a) Percheron. (b) Belgian. (c) Clydesdale. (d) Suffolk.

IX

Some breeds of European origin. (a) Cleveland Bay. (b) Hackney. (c) Welsh Pony. (d) Thoroughbred.

X

Muybridge and his study of gaits. (a) Portrait of Eadweard Muybridge. (b) Track used by Muybridge for taking successive action pictures of horses. Cameras, one for each exposure to be made, were housed in the shed to the right. The horse to be photographed moved in front of the cameras along the track in the middle, where there are devices for tripping the shutters in succession. (c) Typically erroneous representation of the gallop before Muybridge's work. (d) Some of Muybridge's photographs of a galloping Thoroughbred.

XI

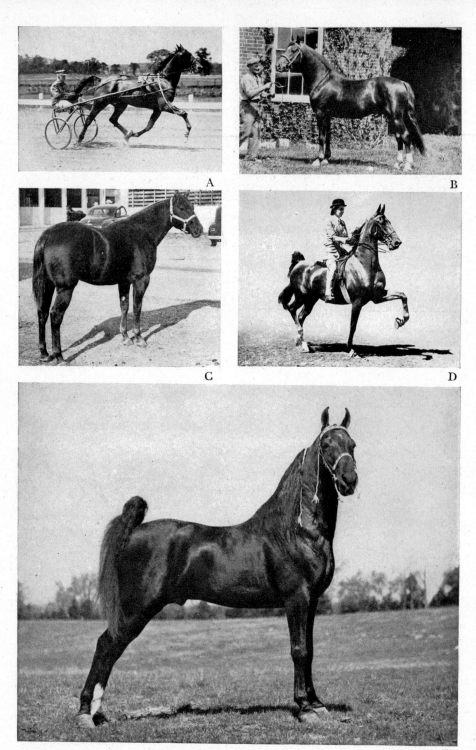

American breeds of horses. (a) Standard Bred. (b) Morgan. (c) Quarter Horse. (d) American Saddle Horse. (e) Tennessee Walking Horse.

XII

B

D

C

A

Color patterns in horses. (a) Palomino. (b) Pinto. (c) Appaloosa. (d) Albino (so-called, or 'Albino W').

XIII

(a) Owen's figure of the first skull of *Hyracotherium*, found by Richardson in 1839. (b-d) Early students of horse ancestry: (b) V. Kovalevsky, 1842-83; (c) T. H. Huxley, 1825-95; (d) Joseph Leidy, 1823-91.

XIV

Students of horse ancestry. (a) O. C. Marsh, 1831-99. (b) E. D. Cope, 1840-97. (c) H. F. Osborn, 1857-1935.

XV

C

A

B

Students of horse ancestry and of evolution. (a) W. D. Matthew, 1871-1930. (b) W. B. Scott, 1858-1947. (c) Charles Darwin, 1809-82.

XVI

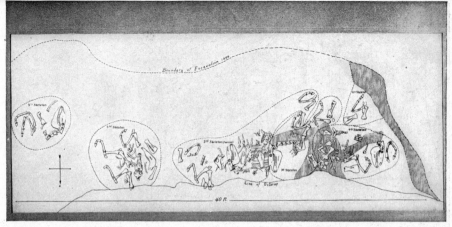

A

B

Collecting fossil horses. (a) Field diagram showing scattered skeletons of fossil horses (*Equus scotti*) in an American Museum quarry at Rock Creek, Texas. (b) An early American Museum field party searching for eohippus in badlands of the Bighorn Basin, Wyoming.

XVII

A

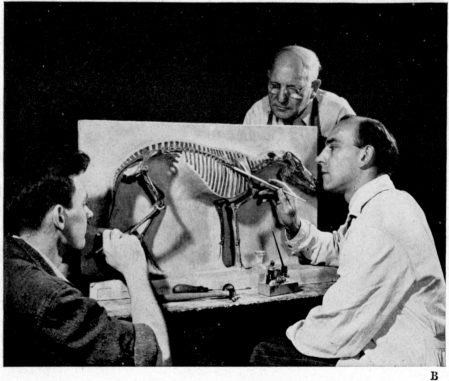

B

XVIII   Collecting and mounting fossil horses. (a) Skeleton of a fossil horse (*Hypohippus*) as found in the rock; much of the skeleton has been exposed and is ready for application of plaster and bandages; the skull is to the upper right. (b) Putting finishing touches on a mounted skeleton of eohippus.

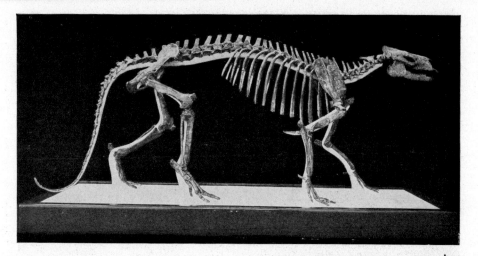

A

B

A condylarth, *Phenacodus,* representing the general group from which the horse family arose. (a) Skeleton. (b) Restoration.

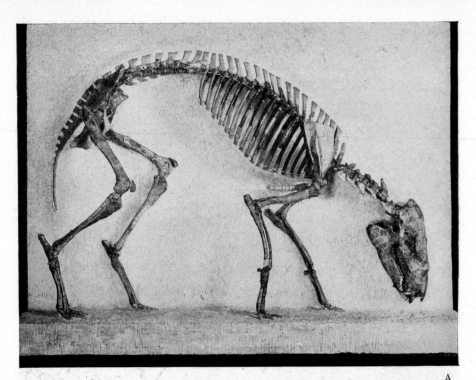

A

B

XX The earliest known member of the horse family, eohippus (= *Hyracotherium*). (a) Skeleton. (b) Restoration.

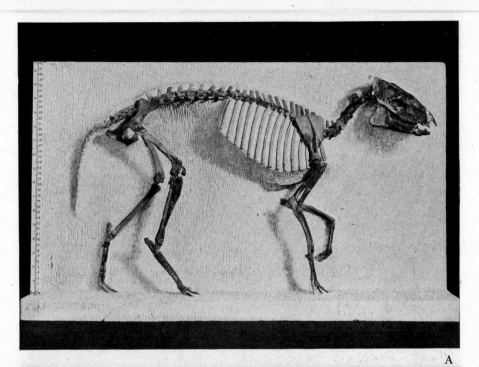

A

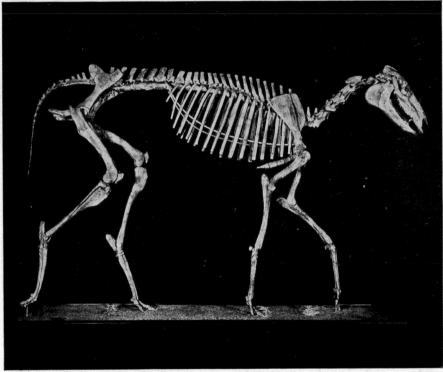

B

Two fossil horse skeletons. (a) *Orohippus*, Eocene. (b) *Miohippus*, Oligocene.

XXI

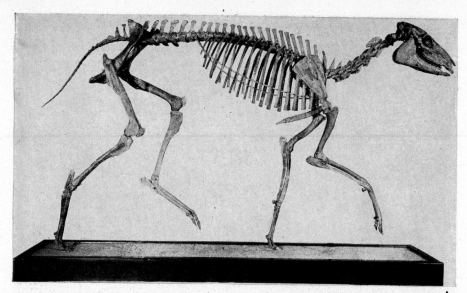

A

B

An Oligocene horse, *Mesohippus*. (a) Skeleton. (b) Restoration.

XXII

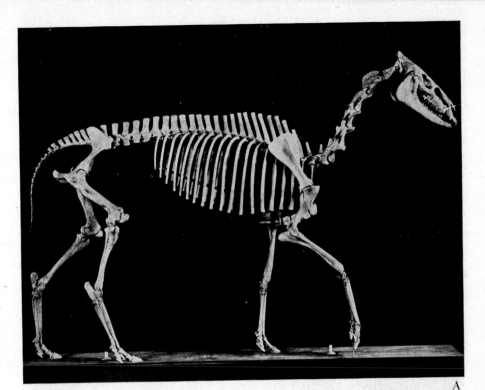

A

B

A Miocene browsing horse, *Hypohippus*. (a) Skeleton. (b) Restoration.

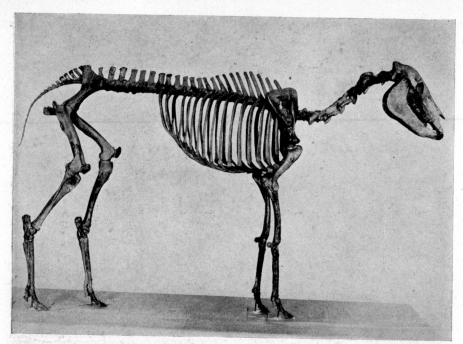

A

B

A Miocene grazing horse, *Merychippus*. (a) Skeleton. (b) Restoration.

XXIV

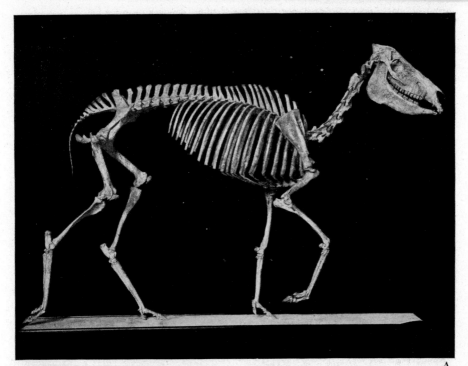

A

A Pliocene three-toed horse, *Neohipparion*. (a) Skeleton. (b) Restoration.

B

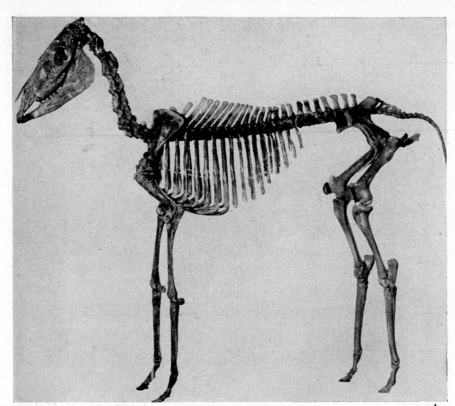

A

B

The first one-toed horse, *Pliohippus*. (a) Skeleton. (b) Restoration.

XXVI

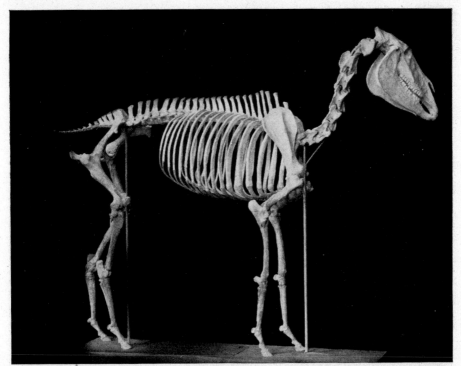

A

B

A primitive and zebra-like *Equus*, subgenus *Plesippus*. (a) Skeleton. (b) Restoration.

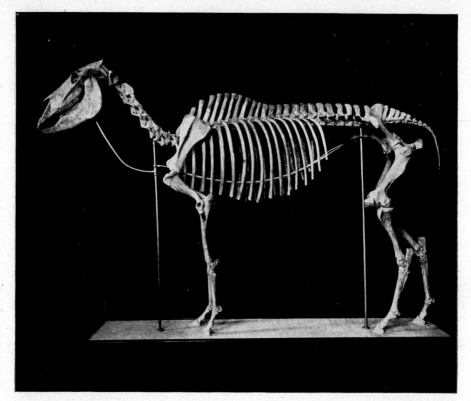

A

B

A true horse of the Ice Age, *Equus*, subgenus *Equus*. (a) Skeleton. (b) Restoration.

XXVIII

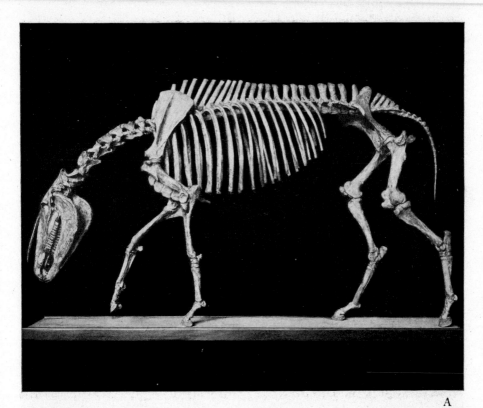

A

B

South American fossil horse, *Hippidion*. (a) Skeleton. (b) Restoration.

A

B

Extinct relatives of the horse. (a) A titanothere, *Brontotherium*. (b) A chalicothere, *Moropus* (four larger animals; in right foreground is an entelodont, so-called 'giant pig,' *Dinohyus,* and in left foreground are small fossil rhinoceroses, *Diceratherium*).

XXX

A

B

Living relatives of the horse. (a) South American tapir and young. (b) African black rhinoceros, pair and young.

XXXI

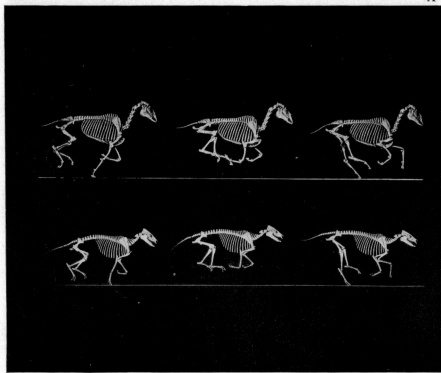

(a) Restoration of a South American pseudo-horse, *Diadiaphorus*. (b) Comparison of skeletons of eohippus and of *Equus*, posed in phases of the gallop. (Not to scale; eohippus is, of course, much smaller than *Equus*.)

XXXII

TEXT FIGURES

(Credits and data additional to those in the captions are given here. A.M.N.H. = The American Museum of Natural History. I.C. = Illustrators Corps. The author is responsible for scientific planning and data in illustrations by I.C.)

TITLE PAGE. Thoroughbred yearlings frolicking at Danny Shea's Merryland Farm. Photograph by William L. Klender, the Sun Papers

1. Horse skull, lower jaw, and dentition. A.M.N.H. drawing for the late Prof. H. F. Osborn, modified by I.C. for present purposes   12

2. Grinding surfaces of horse teeth, with parts labeled. New, A.M.N.H., I.C.   16

3. Heads of the various sorts of living Equidae. New, A.M.N.H., I.C.   19

4. Past and present geographic distribution of wild Equidae. New, A.M.N.H., I.C.   20

5. Diagram of the gaits of the horse. New, A.M.N.H., I.C. Based in part on data from Muybridge. Mode of presentation suggested in part by a diagram by Dr. E. J. Slijper, Utrecht   55

6. Color inheritance in the horse. Pure bay x bay crossing. New, A.M.N.H., I.C. Involving data from Dr. W. E. Castle   78

7. Color inheritance in the horse. Mixed bay x bay crossing. New, A.M.N.H., I.C. Involving data from Dr. W. E. Castle   78

8. Color inheritance in the horse. Palomino x palomino. New, A.M.N.H., I.C. Involving data from Dr. W. E. Castle   79

9. Marsh's phylogeny of the horse. After O. C. Marsh   90

10. Huxley's sketch of 'Eohippus and Eohomo.' From sketch by T. H. Huxley in the Peabody Museum of Natural History, Yale University   90

11. Geologic time scale of horse history. New, A.M.N.H., I.C. Field scenes (left column) based on paintings by John C. Germann for A.M.N.H.   100

12. Comparison of *Phenacodus*, a condylarth, and eohippus. New,

A.M.N.H., I.C. Including data by W. D. Matthew and others in A.M.N.H. files and collections 109

13 (and end papers). The lineage of horses. New, A.M.N.H., I.C. 114

14. Upper cheek teeth of Eocene horses. After W. D. Matthew in A.M.N.H. publications, redrawn and rearranged by I.C. 122

15. Upper cheek teeth of some Oligocene and Miocene horses. Rearranged and in part redrawn by I.C. after H. F. Osborn and W. D. Matthew in A.M.N.H. publications and files 126

16. Sections of low- and high-crowned horse teeth. New, A.M.N.H., I.C., from specimens 134

17. Upper grinding teeth of grazing (high-crowned) Miocene and Pliocene horses. New arrangement by A.M.N.H., I.C., of figures by Dr. R. A. Stirton, University of California 139

18. Curvature of horse teeth. New arrangement by A.M.N.H., I.C., of figures by R. A. Stirton 144

19. Skull of *Pliohippus* with facial pit. After W. K. Gregory, A.M.N.H. 144

20. The wanderings of horses. New, A.M.N.H., I.C. 147

21. Adaptive radiation of horse relatives. New, A.M.N.H., I.C. Restorations after H. F. Osborn, A.M.N.H. and U.S. Geological Survey 152

22. Cuvier's drawings of *Palaeotherium* skeleton and restoration. After Cuvier 153

23. Feet of true, one-toed horse and of South American one-toed pseudo-horse. New, A.M.N.H., I.C., data from W. D. Matthew and from specimens 159

24. Evolutionary series of horse skulls. New, A.M.N.H., I.C., data from H. F. Osborn, Herman Burmeister, and specimens 175

25. Transformation of horse skull. Drawn by A.M.N.H., I.C., but wholly based on technique and illustrations by D'Arcy W. Thompson 176

26. Evolution of the horse brain. Redrawn and rearranged by A.M.N.H., I.C., after Dr. Tilly Edinger 177

27. Molarization of premolars in Eocene horses. Redrawn by I.C. after Dr. Walter Granger, A.M.N.H. 184

28. Evolution of horse upper molars. New arrangement by A.M.N.H., I.C., of figures by R. A. Stirton and W. D. Matthew 187

29. Comparison of eohippus and whippet. New, A.M.N.H., I.C. 191

30. Evolution of horse feet. After W. D. Matthew, A.M.N.H. 194

31. Selected stages in evolution of the horse forefoot. New, A.M.N.H., I.C., data from H. F. Osborn and specimens 195

32. Foot mechanics and evolution in horses. Redrawn and rearranged by A.M.N.H., I.C., after C. L. Camp and N. Smith, University of California   196

33. Vertical section of toe of recent horse. Previously unpublished drawing by L. M. Sterling for H. F. Osborn, A.M.N.H.   196

34. Evolution of bones of the forearm and gaskin. After W. D. Matthew, A.M.N.H.   202

INTRODUCTION

A LEARNED Arab has told us that paradise on earth is to be found on the back of a horse, in the pages of a book, and in the arms of a woman. A book about horses should, then, rate as one and a half terrestrial paradises, at least. Such must be the opinion of many writers, although it may not be shared by all their readers. Probably no other one group of animals has been the subject of so much writing, ranging from ponderous tomes to frivolous limericks.

Horses figure in the very oldest graphic records made by man, Stone Age paintings made long before writing was invented. They will also figure largely in tomorrow's newspaper. Between these dates, a roster of writers who have discussed horses would include most of the great names of literature and many of the great and humble among scientists and lovers of life and nature. Homer and Aristotle, Shakespeare and Cuvier, Cervantes and Darwin, all these and many more have devoted attention to the horse, and many others will doubtless do so in the future. The subject is fascinating and inexhaustible.

An aspirant to enter this distinguished and numerous company should satisfy himself and his reader in regard to two questions. Among the multitude of topics concerning horses, which are to be discussed? And on these topics, what is there to say that has not already been better said?

This is a book about horses as animals. Something will, of course, be said about horses in the service and for the pleasure of mankind, because those are important aspects of this particular animal. But, throughout, the center of interest is to be the animal and not its use. Thoroughbreds will be described, but not handicapping or betting systems. Gaits will be listed and explained, but not styles of riding or types of harness and saddles. Coat colors and something about their inheritance will be reviewed, but not the market value of palominos.

An important reason why horses are so fascinating and why there is so much to say about them is that they are such representative animals. From horses we may learn not only about the horse itself but also about animals in general, indeed about ourselves and about life as a whole, its history and characteristics. The aim of this book is not only to present the members of the horse family, but also to present an introduction to the study of animals and of life, with horses providing concrete and excellent examples. Reading about horses is one of the best ways to begin on many other subjects of great interest and importance: how animals are classified, the relationships between their structure and their ways of life, their variations and their breeding, how fossils are found and what they mean, the history of the earth, the evolution of life and its principles.

There are three main approaches to the study of animals, all of which are superlatively illustrated by the horse family. First is the study of wild, living animals, their characteristics, distribution, habits, and the like. Then there is the study of animal breeds and breeding, relationships to man, domestication, and related subjects. Finally, and not least important, there is the historical approach, not history in the strictly human sense, which belongs under the first two headings, but history against the broader background of the history of the earth and its life. This book is an attempt to summarize modern knowledge in all three of these interconnected fields.

Popular interest in horses arises mainly from the fact that they are admirable animals with which everyone has some acquaintance. Still more interesting and important are aspects that are less familiar and, therefore, require more extended explanation. If horses had just happened or had dropped from the skies, we should admire but not understand. They did not just happen. They developed; they evolved from more ancient forms of life. Their presence among us and their various characteristics have rhyme and reason.

It is evolution that gives rhyme and reason to the story of the horse family as it exists today and as it existed in the past. Our own existence has the same rhyme and reason, and so has the existence of every other living organism. One of the main points of interest in the horse family is that it so clearly demonstrates this tremendously important fact. Many other evolutionary sequences are now known, but the beautiful series of ancient and modern horses displayed in many museums are still the simplest way to convince any open-minded person that evolution is a fact. You can see it with your own eyes. That is one reason why there is perennial interest not only in the horses of today but also in their ancestry.

There are other reasons, too. Even though we no longer need to wonder whether evolution is true or not—no real student of horse history now doubts this for a moment—we still are not sure precisely how and why evolution has occurred. It is one matter to know that a thing is so, and quite another matter to understand how it operates and why it is so. For instance, you know that an airplane flies, but are you sure you know all about what holds it up and why? The story of the horse family provides one of the best means for studying the how and why of evolution.

The story is interesting for its own sake, too. Everyone finds the living horse familiar, useful, and likable, and everyone feels some fascination in the story of where it came from and how horses gradually changed from eohippus to the animal we have today. A fossil tooth or bone is certainly a dull and uninspiring object if it is looked at in the wrong way. (I am tempted to let out the secret that even professional students of fossils do not always look at them in the right way.) The wrong way is to look at fossils as something dead and petrified, to measure and describe them as if they were pieces of rock, to compare them bit by bit and to slap new names on those that look a little different, with never a thought for the processes and meanings behind those differences.

The right way is to see fossils as forms of life. They are animals, just as full of life as you are, even though they occur at different points in the endless stream of time. Within their own segments of this stream, they breathe, eat, drink, breed, fight, and lead their own lives as you do yours in the segment you call 'now.' The shapes of their teeth and bones are part of their living, and by the proper study of those shapes we can re-create much of that life for our own diversion and instruction. The shapes vary and they change as we follow them along in the time stream. The changes are full of meaning if we remember that they are changes not merely in shape but also in life. The changes lead up to the horses of now, and in them, too, we see meaningful form and understand it the better as the result of the long history revealed by fossils.

It is my duty to warn you that we do not know all there is to know about fossil horses or about the horses of today. A great deal is known. We know that the horses did evolve and we can follow the most important changes during this evolution. We know the essentials of the anatomy of modern horses, we can name and describe most of their breeds, and we know much about how they reproduce, grow, and live. We do not yet know all the details of just how the horses evolved, and we still have a large amount to learn about why they evolved. We do not know nearly enough about how the various characteristics of modern breeds are transmitted and developed in their offspring or about many other aspects of the living animals.

The bonediggers are still at work gathering more specimens of fossil horses, and paleontologists are still measuring, arranging, and studying these in many laboratories throughout the world. Scientific breeders and physiologists are still crossing, recording, and experimenting. Every year we know a little more, but I do not suppose that we shall ever know literally everything about horses, or anything else. In the following pages I have tried to stick closely to established facts and to conclusions from those facts endorsed at present by the best qualified students. Of course, the future may show that even those students are wrong on some points. It is also more than likely that I have made some blunders in trying to cover so large a subject. When it is clear that some point is doubtful, it is omitted if it seems unimportant. Doubtful points or personal opinions that require mention are labeled as such, and other possibilities on these points are also mentioned.

Now to begin the story. A good way to start a discussion is to tell what you are talking about; so the best way to begin a book on horses seems to be with the question, 'What is a horse?'

Part One

LIVING HORSES

1

WHAT IS A HORSE?

SIMPLEST questions often have the most complicated answers, and there is no really simple answer to the question, 'What is a horse?' A technical student of horses might reply, 'A horse is a member of the species *Equus caballus,* or of the genus *Equus,* or of the family Equidae.' That is really three different answers, and yet it is no answer at all, because it only names a species, a genus, and the family of horses and does not say what they are. Someone else might reply, 'Why, everybody knows what a horse is!' and that is no answer, either.

The technical answer is better, but it requires explanation. From sad experience, zoologists early found that everyone does not know what a horse, or a rat, or a cat is. These common names do well enough in rough and ready conversation, but they are inadequate for precise and scientific use. The word 'horse' originally meant the domestic horse. It is still used mainly in that sense, just because these are the horses we usually talk about in ordinary conversation, but then there are wild horses, too. How are we to indicate that they are a sort of horse, and yet not the same as the domestic horse? Then there are donkeys, zebras, onagers, and others that are horse-like, really in one sense kinds of horses, but not the same as domestic or wild horses. We need some way to indicate that they are horses of a sort and yet that they are not domestic horses and differ more from domestic horses than wild horses do. At least they do have common names, but the situation really becomes complicated when we begin talking about some of the extinct horses, eohippus for example, which are definitely not horses in the strictest sense, or

3

donkeys, zebras, onagers, or any other kind for which there is a common name.

The zoologists' solution of this difficulty is a device called the Linnaean hierarchy, 'Linnaean' because it was put in essentially its present form by the great Swedish naturalist Linnaeus in the 18th century, and 'hierarchy' (meaning a series of higher and lower systematic grades) because it arranges animals in larger or smaller groups according to their degrees of resemblance and relationship. Each group is given a special name, and by using these names the zoologist can designate precisely what group he means and what general degree of resemblance and relationship is involved. The main steps in this series, from largest to smallest, are Kingdom, Phylum, Class, Order, Family, Genus, and Species. When needed for greater precision, some other steps can be inserted, such as Subfamily, Subgenus, or Subspecies. The system can readily be understood by seeing how the domestic horse fits into this scheme:

KINGDOM ANIMALIA—Includes all animals, in the broadest sense of anything alive that is not a plant, from amoeba to man.

PHYLUM CHORDATA—Includes all animals that have a stiff rod down the back (along with other peculiarities) and especially the vertebrates, or animals with jointed backbones: fishes, amphibians, reptiles, birds, and mammals.

CLASS MAMMALIA—Includes all the chordates or vertebrates that give milk, have hair, are warm-blooded, etc., among them man himself, and most of the creatures called 'animals' in popular speech, such as horses, cows, dogs, monkeys, rats, etc.

ORDER PERISSODACTYLA—Includes mammals that have hoofs (usually), with the weight mainly carried by the middle hoof when there are more than one, that eat plants, and that have various other peculiarities showing that all are descended from an eohippus-like common ancestry. Besides the horses, it includes the tapirs and rhinoceroses among living animals and extinct groups called palaeotheres, titanotheres, and chalicotheres.

FAMILY EQUIDAE—The 'horse family,' in a broad sense, including all the living horses, donkeys, zebras, and onagers, all their ancestors back to eohippus, and other extinct derivatives from this ancestral line.

GENUS EQUUS—Includes all the living members of the family Equidae and their immediate ancestors and close relatives during the last Ice Age. *Equus* is simply the Latin word for 'horse.' Horses, strictly speaking, belong to the typical sub-genus of *Equus* while the donkeys, zebras, and onagers may be placed in three distinct subgenera within the genus. (Some authorities call these different genera, but whether to call them genera or subgenera is mainly a matter of taste and sense of proportion, and makes no real difference.)

SPECIES EQUUS CABALLUS—Includes only the domestic horse and its wild relatives so closely related that they can (or could) interbreed with it and produce fertile offspring. The only recently living true wild horses are best designated as subspecies of *Equus caballus*. There are, of course, also many different breeds, strains, and types of domestic horses.

Note that a group larger than a species has a single name, like the genus *Equus*, but that a species, such as *Equus caballus*, has two names, the first of which is the name of the genus to which it belongs. Names of genera and species are usually printed in italics. Names of families always end '-idae' and are formed by adding this ending to the root of the name of a genus typical of the family. Thus you belong to the species *Homo sapiens* and *Homo* is the type genus of the human family Hominidae.

The technical names applied to animals in connection with this Linnaean hierarchy are coined by zoologists, usually from Latin or Greek roots although other sources or even arbitrarily invented words may be used. Once established, these names are not subject to change and their employment is world-wide among zoologists. The domestic horse is *Equus caballus* to all students, even though in their own languages they may call the animal 'horse,' 'pferd,' 'cheval,' 'caballo,' or any of hundreds of other radically different names.

Now the statement that a horse is 'a member of the species *Equus caballus*, or of the genus *Equus*, or of the family Equidae' begins to make sense. We no longer have to use such clumsy and vague expressions as 'horses, strictly speaking,' or 'the horses in a broad sense,' but can easily designate just which horses we mean and how much variety we mean to include. In the first part of this book, about living horses, 'horse' generally means *Equus caballus*, but in referring to ancient horses and the evolution of the horse, the word usually refers to any member of the horse family, Equidae. When the meaning is not obvious, a more precise name is used.

Most members of the horse family are extinct. This is not surprising when it is remembered that the family is about 60 million years
old and that it has been constantly moving about, changing, and
splitting up into different lines throughout that long period of time.
By a conservative count, about twenty broad kinds, genera, of horses
are known only as fossils. These will be discussed in the second part
of this book. All the living Equidae, varied as they are, represent a
single genus, *Equus*. In this genus there are six species: one for the
domestic horses and their closest wild relatives, one for the asses, domestic and wild, one for the onagers, and three for different kinds
of zebras.

2

A LOOK AT 'EQUUS'

MODERN industrial designers have taught us to see beauty in things properly constructed to serve a particular function. A horse, too, is a beautiful example of functionalism. The living species of *Equus* are almost perfectly designed to meet the needs of their ways of life, and most of the features in which they differ from other animals can be interpreted as functional adaptations to their special habits. We shall see, when we look at the ancestry of *Equus*, how this design was developed and how, too, the function sometimes changed and the design changed with it. Before discussing differences between the various species of wild horses and breeds and types of domestic horses, let us briefly consider the essentials of the basic design of *Equus*, in which all these living members of the horse family agree.

Man has taken the natural design of *Equus* and has modified it in various ways, by selective breeding, to serve his own purposes. To run races, he has bred slender animals somewhat (not much) faster than any wild horses, and to pull loads he has bred heavy horses somewhat (again not much) more powerful than any of their wild relatives. He has not been able to change the horse in any really essential way, not nearly as much, for instance, as the breeders have been able to change the dog. Wild species and races of *Equus* differ in details of design, from the striped zebra to the sandy Asiatic wild horse or the tough little wild ass, but even these are merely superficial variations of the same fundamental design. This design is adapted to roaming and running on the hard soil of plains, eating harsh grasses, and escaping enemies by a burst of speed.

The design for speed is striking, whether we look at the compact body, sleek except for the fly-whisk tail and the mane (not well-developed in wild species), or whether we look deeper at the bones and muscles. The great running muscles are bunched at the upper parts of the legs, where they give maximum motion of the leg with relatively short motion of the muscles. The legs are long and slender and ensure extra speed by the fact that the lower parts, more distant from the body, are particularly elongated. To increase the stride still more, the horse stands permanently on tiptoe, with only the point of the one toe, with its stout, hard hoof, touching the ground. (See Plates I and II)

Compare this design with that of a slow-moving animal like man, for instance. Our legs are longer in the upper part than in the lower and the muscles are distributed far down the leg and even bunched heavily (if, at times, prettily) in the calf. Our heel normally touches the ground. (The horse's 'heel' is its hock, half-way up the leg, and never touches the ground.) We rise on tiptoe with effort and only in the stress of stealth or for a short burst of what we consider speed but a horse would not. The horse's leg bones, fore and hind, also form keeled and pulley joints that eliminate the freedom of side-ward motion so useful to us, but useless and inefficient in an animal that uses its 'arms' and legs mainly for running.

The rather long neck and large, especially long head of *Equus* enable it to reach its food, low grass, while standing alert and ready for instant flight. The eyes, set far back in the head, remain high enough to spot an approaching enemy even while the lips and front teeth are cropping low grass. The rounded cranium lodges a fairly large and complex central office, the brain, for the operation of this whole intricate and beautiful mechanism.

To speak of a horse, as some misguided horselovers do, as having 'almost human' intelligence is nonsense because the brightest horse is abysmally stupid in comparison with the dullest normal man. *Equus* is, however, highly intelligent as animals go, and the motor co-ordination achieved by its nervous system seems to be better than in most men. The complexity of its brain is concerned more with this function than with intelligence in the strictly human sense. This matter of intelligence in the horse will probably long be disputed among horsemen and among scientific students of animal behavior. A few sentimentalists imagine that horses' mental processes are much the same as our own and that they lack little but the power of speech. On the other hand, a few extreme and rigid students maintain that the horse has no real thought or even consciousness in the human sense and that the horses' actions are entirely automatic, by instinct or by conditioned reflexes. It is fairly certain that neither of these views is correct and that the truth lies between them. Unfortunately we cannot put ourselves inside a horse and observe how it really feels, thinks, and acts. If we could, it is my opinion that we would find that we, as horses, were truly conscious of ourselves and the world about us and that we modified our behavior by dim processes of memory and even by crude reasoning, but that many of our actions occurred without our thinking of them in advance and that our thought processes as a whole were simpler than and almost unrecognizably different from those of men.

At this point someone is sure to remark on 'educated' horses, sometimes exhibited, which are apparently able to spell, count, add, and do even more complicated operations that seem to require intelligence of a very human sort. These tricks speak well for the sort of sensory-motor co-ordination in which horses do excel, but they are not acts of human-like intelligence. It has been well established by carefully controlled study that these tricks do not depend on the ability to recognize numbers or letters or to count. The horse is really reacting to cues given, sometimes unconsciously, by the trainer, almost imperceptible movements or changes in tone of voice, which are recognized by the horse with extraordinary acuteness. A high degree of ability is shown, certainly, but it is a thoroughly horsy ability, not human intelligence—and why should it be otherwise?

Even without considering relative degrees of intelligence, we can be sure that the world is a very different place to a horse from what it is to a man. Our conception of things and our thoughts about them are profoundly influenced by the senses that gather information for us. In both horses and men, the most important of these senses is vision, but the eyes of horses and men are markedly different. The perceptions of things seen must also be very different. It is impossible to say that horses or men have better eyes in general. In some ways horses seem to have better vision, and in some ways men. Both have excellent eyes for their own decidedly distinct needs.

Horses are famous for the sharpness of their vision, whether by day or by night. An Arabian fable published by Rochon-Duvigneaud, a leading student of vision in animals, relates that a lion and a horse had a contest to determine which had the better vision. On a dark night, the lion was able to see a white pearl in milk. The horse could see a black pearl in coal. The judges gave the palm to the horse. Less fabulously, it is claimed that Arabian horses can distinguish their masters from other men dressed similarly, at distances up to a quarter of a mile or more. This acuteness of vision is probably related to the great size of a horse's eye. No other land mammal has so large an eye in absolute dimensions, although many smaller animals, including the horse's own ancestors, have larger eyes in comparison with the size of the whole body.

In spite of its acuteness, the horse's eye does not have variable focus, or accommodation, as does the human eye. Objects at different distances cannot be brought into sharp focus at the same part of the retina. Near and distant objects are in focus, and hence can be seen clearly, only on different parts of the retina, and therefore must be observed at somewhat different angles if they are to be seen sharply. A horse's eye has no fovea, the spot of especially acute vision where we focus anything, near or far, on which our attention is concentrated.

Horses have binocular vision, that is, they can look at objects with both eyes at once, as we do, but this ability is not as well developed as in man. Almost our whole field of vision is binocular and, unlike the horse, we point both eyes directly at an object when we look at it. In the horse there is only a relatively narrow binocular zone in the direction in which the head is pointed, and the eyes diverge even when both are looking at the same thing. On the other hand, each separate eye in the horse has an extraordinarily wide sweep. Because his eye takes in a sweep of a complete semicircle a horse can see straight backward and straight forward at the same time, without

moving the head or eye. The horse's eye is also so built that it emphasizes any motion toward the edge of the field of vision. A horse is
sharply sensitive to a moving object far around to the side or even
behind the direction in which the animal is heading. This ability is
certainly of great value to wild horses. They usually live in open
country where vision and flight are the best defense, and any moving
object behind them is likely to be dangerous. It is unfortunate that
this peculiarity, which helped the horse's wild ancestors to survive,
is a disadvantage to the rider or driver of a domestic horse. Many a
rider has learned to his sorrow that his mount is startled by a sudden
motion on the side or rear and that the horse's normal reaction is to
break into flight.

Another interesting adaptation reflecting the importance of lateral
vision to the horse is the fact that when the pupil contracts it does
not become a smaller ellipse or circle, as in man, but becomes a rectangle, elongated horizontally.

It is not yet surely established whether horses have color vision.
This is a difficult point to determine in animals. Often when we
think they are distinguishing colors they are really reacting to what
seem to them different degrees of brightness, not of color. Most mammals other than monkeys and men seem to be color blind, and this
is probably true of the horse. The man in the story who tried to
keep a horse happy on a diet of straw by dyeing the straw green was
probably wasting his time.

Domestic horses are often near-sighted. Various investigators have
found that 20 to 40 per cent of the horses studied were near-sighted.
It is a widespread belief that near-sighted horses are more skittish
than others, especially if they are more near-sighted in one eye than
in the other. I do not know how true this may be. A related folk-tale
has it that horses are timid because their eyes magnify and everything looks larger to them. This is so illogical that it is commonly
used by psychologists as one of a series of absurdities in an intelligence test.

Wild animals, as far as their eyes have been studied, are seldom
near-sighted and are more likely to be a little far-sighted, if anything.
Wild horses apparently have not been extensively investigated re-

garding this point, but it is unlikely that they are as often near-sighted as are domestic horses. Domestication with its attendant in-breeding frequently introduces disturbances in normal functioning of the eyes and other organs.

Less is known about other senses of the horse than about vision. The senses of smell and of hearing both appear to be very keen,

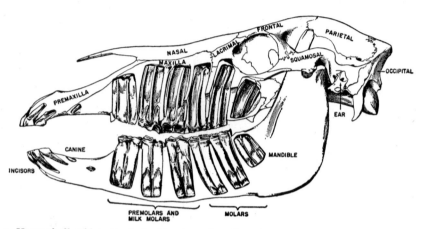

1. Horse skull and teeth. Left side view of modern horse skull and lower jaw, with main bones and groups of teeth labeled. The bone has been cut away to show the lengths of the parts of teeth still embedded in the jaw. In the lower jaw, the last remnants of the three milk molars are still in place and the large, permanent pre-molars are pushing up below them. In the upper jaw, remnants of only the last two milk molars are still in place.

probably more so than in man, although horses usually seem to place more reliance on their eyes than on their noses or ears.

Legs for running and eyes for warning have enabled horses to survive through the ages although subject to constant attack by flesh-eaters that liked nothing better than horse for supper. Horses too have to eat and their most important structures in this connection are their teeth. (See Plate IIIa, b, and Fig. 1) It is well to have a par-ticularly good look at the teeth, not only because they are one of the most important parts of the design of *Equus*, but also because teeth are the commonest and most easily classified fossil fragments of horses and are used most extensively in the study of horse evolution.

People who insist on looking a gift horse in the mouth see first a set of front teeth, which are called incisors. There are twelve of these teeth in adults, three on each side in the upper jaw and three on each side in the lower jaw. The ones farthest forward, on each side of the midline, are the first incisors, while the second incisors are next to and outside these, and the third incisors are the last ones, outside and toward the back. (Some horsemen call the first, second, and third incisors the central, middle, and corner teeth.) Colts have milk or baby teeth, just as young humans do, and these begin to be shed when the animal is about two and a half years old. The milk incisors are somewhat smaller and, especially, shorter than the permanent incisors, and the first and second permanent incisors have grooves on the outer face, lacking on the milk incisors. Both milk and permanent incisors are simple teeth, somewhat like curved chisels, except that they have a deep fold or pocket that forms a cup or 'mark' on the wearing surface. These cups do not extend clear down to the root, and so when the top of the tooth is worn off the cups eventually disappear.

It is mainly by the replacement and wear of the lower incisors that horsemen judge the age of a horse. (See Plate III) This is how it is done:

Condition of Lower Incisors	Age (approximately)
First milk incisors present, others absent	Birth to 2 or 3 weeks
First and second milk incisors present, third absent	2 or 3 weeks to 6 months
All milk incisors present, and:	
All with cups	6 months to 1 year
First without cups, second and third with cups	1-1½ years
First and second without, third with cup	1½-2 years
None with cups	2-2½ years
First permanent and second and third milk incisors	2½-3½ years
First and second permanent and third milk incisors	3½-4½ years
All permanent incisors present, and:	
All with cups	4½-7 years
First without, second and third with cups	7-8 years
First and second without, third with cup	8-9 years

[Continued on next page

Condition of Lower Incisors	Age (approximately)
None with cups, and:	
Wear surface of first incisor wider (side-to-side) than deep (fore and aft)	9-18 years
Wear surface of first incisor deeper than wide	Over 18 years

Do not expect these ages to work out exactly. Individual horses vary considerably in the rate of replacement and wear of the teeth and skillful horse traders do not judge age entirely on this basis, but this is an easy way to get a reasonably good idea of age. (It is also a regrettable fact that traders have been known to change the apparent age of the incisors by pulling some, filing them down, or making artificial cups in them.)

In male horses a small, pointed, somewhat tusk-like tooth, the canine, occurs a short distance behind the incisors in each jaw. It is commonly lacking in mares, or, if present, is just a small vestige.

Behind the incisors and canine (if this is present) there is a toothless space in each jaw—this is where the bit is placed on domestic horses. This is followed, in adult horses (four to five years and older), by a set of six large teeth in each side of each jaw, collectively called the grinding teeth or cheek teeth. In the recent horses these teeth all look almost exactly alike except that they curve somewhat differently and the end teeth (first and last in the series of six) have the grinding surfaces more triangular than the others. We shall see, however, that in the remote ancestors of the horse the first three of these teeth were markedly different from the last three. The first three are also preceded by milk teeth and the last three are not. These differences make it necessary to distinguish two sorts of teeth in this series. The first three are called 'premolars' and the last three are called 'molars.' (See Fig. 1) In the earlier horses there was another, simpler premolar in front of those regularly present in the modern horse, so that most fossil horses have seven cheek teeth, four premolars, and three molars. The three usual premolars of the modern horse are really the second, third, and fourth premolars. Even now, however, the first premolar is not completely eliminated. It occasionally occurs as a vestige, a mere nubbin, which horsemen call 'the wolf tooth.'

All these cheek teeth have the form of very high columns or prisms when they are first formed. As they are worn off by use, they keep moving out of the jaw (down in the upper jaw and up in the lower jaw) so as always to maintain a grinding surface at the same level. Finally, in very old horses, they are worn right down to the roots and can no longer grind food—in wild horses this puts a limit on the possible length of life, for a horse cannot survive when it can no longer grind its food, but few horses live to this stage anyway. Domestic horses in their twenties are old, but it is not too uncommon for them to reach their thirties and horses have been known to live into their forties.

A look at the working surface of these cheek teeth shows a complicated pattern formed by low, twisting ridges of a hard substance, enamel, standing up from a background or filling of two softer materials, dentine and cement. The relative hardness of the enamel makes it continue to stand up in ridges as the whole tooth is worn down. The precise pattern formed by these ridges is one of the best ways to tell the various kinds of fossil horses apart. To make their description shorter and more precise in technical studies, all the various parts of the pattern have been given special names. We do not need to bother about these names here, and even in the description of fossil horses we shall be concerned mainly with the gradual change of the pattern as a whole, but for the convenience of students the names are given in the accompanying drawing (Fig. 2).

The whole tooth system of the living horse is a complex and highly specialized mechanism for eating grass. With the aid of the mobile lips, the incisors cut and pull the grass. It is then moved with the help of the tongue to the back part of the mouth, where the jaw muscles have strong leverage, and is there ground fine by the opposing ridges of the upper and lower cheek teeth. Grass is a very harsh food that wears teeth down rapidly. If we, with our low and relatively small teeth, tried to live on grass our teeth would be worn out in a year or so (aside from the fact that our digestive system could not extract our proper nourishment from it), but the large, deep grinding teeth of the horse can stand the wear for as long as horses normally live. We shall see later that early horses could not eat grass and that the perfection of a mechanism for this purpose was one of the most important events in their evolution.

To turn from these details back to *Equus* as a whole, the whole

LAST UPPER PREMOLAR   LAST LOWER PREMOLAR

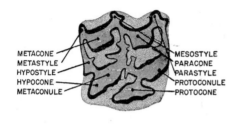

METACONE
METASTYLE
HYPOSTYLE
HYPOCONE
METACONULE

MESOSTYLE
PARACONE
PARASTYLE
PROTOCONULE
PROTOCONE

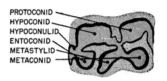

PROTOCONID
HYPOCONID
HYPOCONULID
ENTOCONID
METASTYLID
METACONID

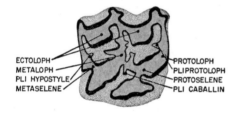

ECTOLOPH
METALOPH
PLI HYPOSTYLE
METASELENE

PROTOLOPH
PLIPROTOLOPH
PROTOSELENE
PLI CABALLIN

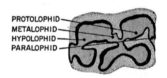

PROTOLOPHID
METALOPHID
HYPOLOPHID
PARALOPHID

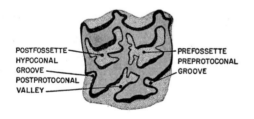

POSTFOSSETTE
HYPOCONAL
GROOVE
POSTPROTOCONAL
VALLEY

PREFOSSETTE
PREPROTOCONAL
GROOVE

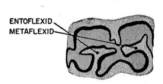

ENTOFLEXID
METAFLEXID

TISSUES { — Enamel / ▒ Cement / ▨ Dentine

2. Grinding surfaces of upper (left) and lower (right) last premolars of modern horse with parts labeled. The upper drawings indicate the main cusps and cones, the middle drawings the principal crests and folds, and the lower drawings some of the basins, valleys, and grooves. The same names are applied to molar teeth.

bodily form, the conformation and points, and the skeleton, which maintains and largely determines this form, are highly characteristic. Here, however, a picture is worth a thousand words, and pictures of *Equus* and its skeleton are given in place of descriptions (Plates I, II).

3

THE LIVING WILD EQUIDAE

THERE are no truly wild horses now in either North or South America. The 'wild horses' of our western states are wild enough, in the ordinary sense of the word, and some of them still exist although their numbers have been much reduced by relentless hunting. Technically, however, these are not really wild horses. In more accurate usage, a wild animal is one whose ancestors have always been wild. A feral animal is one whose ancestors were domesticated but escaped and ran wild. All the American 'wild' horses are derived from domesticated horses, so they are really feral horses. They are, of course, *Equus caballus,* the species to which all domestic horses belong.

In earlier historic times truly wild *Equus caballus* was common from Europe right across central Asia. The Romans met them in Spain, and in the Middle Ages they still existed in the wilder parts of central Europe. The European wild horses, called 'tarpans,' may have survived as late as the twentieth century in eastern Russia, but it is probable that the last survivors had crossed extensively with domestic horses and had long since ceased to represent the pure wild type. In any event, they are now extinct.

It is usually said that the only living true wild horse (that is, wild *Equus caballus*) is the central Asiatic race or subspecies called Przewalski's horse, after a Russian explorer whose name is unfortunately almost unpronounceable in English. It is, however, uncertain that even this race survives today in pure form. It lives, or used to live, mainly in western Mongolia and eastern Turkestan, and it is, or was, similar to a rather small and coarse domestic horse but with

17

a short, erect mane and without a forelock. (See Plate IVa, and Fig. 3)
The color is yellowish or light reddish brown, with dark mane and
tail. This is referred to as 'dun' by many students of horse history
(including Darwin), but it is not the same as the dun of most domestic horses. In a domestic horse, the Przewalski horse color would
more properly be called a light or yellowish bay.

Recent expeditions have often failed to find Przewalski's horses in
the regions where they used to occur, and they may have been ex-
terminated. More likely, they have simply blended with herds of
feral or half-wild domestic horses that roam that region. These Asiatic wild horses crossed freely with domestic horses. It is possible that
the supposed Przewalski's horses seen by modern explorers in central
Asia or exhibited in zoos have had an admixture of domestic horse
blood and that a pure wild race has not existed for some time.

Asia is still the home of another wild species of Equidae, *Equus
hemionus,* which has many 'popular' names: Chigetai, onager, kiang,
kulan, ghor-khar, Asiatic wild ass, etc. (See Plate IVb, and Fig. 3) It
is not really a wild ass and the other names are difficult and confusing in their applications in different regions—you see how much
clearer and simpler it is to use the technical name and call these animals *Equus hemionus.* They look rather like a cross between a horse
and a donkey, but they are not. They are a true-breeding separate
species. They stand about 4 feet (12 hands) high at the shoulders,
and have moderately large ears, a short dark mane, a dark stripe
down the back, and a dark tuft at the end of the donkey-like tail.
Some of them were domesticated in ancient times, but apparently
they were not as good for human purposes as donkeys and horses.
Their domestication was given up when these two domestic forms
spread into the same regions. Wild *Equus hemionus* used to cover
an enormous range, from China clear through central Asia, down
into India, and through Persia to Syria and Palestine. (Omar Khayyam was talking about the Persian *E. hemionus* when he sang: 'And
Bahram, that great hunter—the wild ass stamps o'er his head but
cannot break his sleep.') Alas! This handsome animal, which seems
so symbolic of the freedom of the steppes and deserts of Asia, is suf-
fering the fate of so many of the most striking wild animals. It is

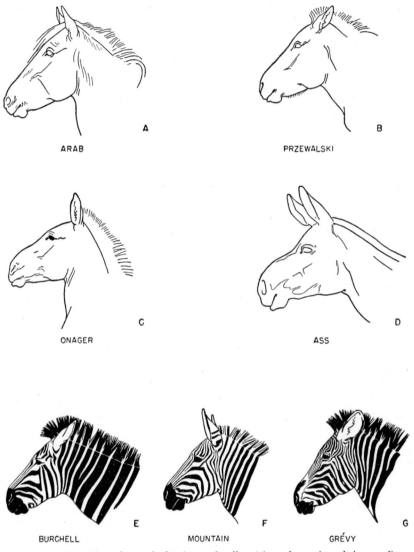

ARAB

PRZEWALSKI

ONAGER

ASS

BURCHELL

MOUNTAIN

GRÉVY

3. Heads of living members of the horse family: (A) a domesticated horse, *Equus caballus caballus*, Arabian breed; (B) Asiatic wild horse, *Equus caballus prjewalskii*; (C) Asiatic onager or so-called wild ass, *Equus hemionus*; (D) true ass, *Equus asinus*; (E) Burchell's zebra, a bontequagga, *Equus quagga burchelli*; (F) Mountain zebra, *Equus zebra*; (G) Grévy's zebra, *Equus grévyi*.

extinct over much of its former range and is probably not common now anywhere.

The true wild asses, *Equus asinus,* ancestors and relatives of our domestic donkeys, were characteristic of northern and northeastern

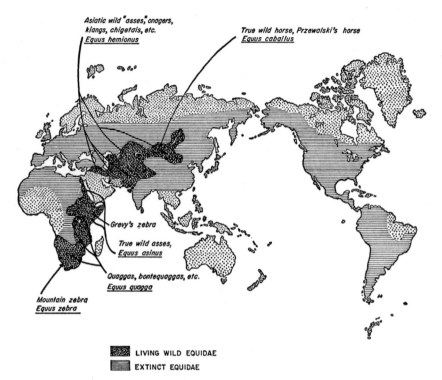

Asiatic wild "asses," onagers,
kiangs, chigetais, etc.
Equus hemionus

True wild horse, Przewalski's horse
Equus caballus

Grevy's zebra

True wild asses,
Equus asinus

Quaggas, bontequaggas, etc.
Equus quagga

Mountain zebra
Equus zebra

LIVING WILD EQUIDAE
EXTINCT EQUIDAE

4. Past and present geographic distribution of wild Equidae. The range of the living species is still being reduced and is probably not now quite as extensive or continuous as shown. The thinly dotted areas have no living wild horses and fossil horses have not been found in them, although the possibility of occurrence is not excluded in all cases.

Africa. (Plate IVc, and Fig. 3) A few still exist in the Sudan, Abyssinia, Somaliland, and perhaps some other regions, but they too have become extinct over most of their former range. As is true also of Przewalski's horse, they interbreed so freely with the domesticated races of the same species that it is difficult to tell whether some herds are really wild or are feral donkeys or hybrids between the two. The true wild asses look like relatively large and strong domestic donkeys, with grayish or ashy upper parts, a dark stripe down the back, and generally a shoulder stripe and variable striping on the legs.

The other living wild Equidae are all often called 'zebras,' but they include several distinct species. They are all striped over part, at least, of the body, but aside from this superficial resemblance they differ and vary so remarkably that students are still quarreling over how many kinds there really are and how they should be classified. This is no place to carry on the quarrel, and I shall distinguish three main kinds and call them species.

Equus quagga includes a variety of different races, some of them seemingly so different that they have often been classed as two or many different species. This is, however, simply a particularly good example of geographical variation in the coloring of a single species of animals. In a general way the northern animals are more striped and the striping becomes less and less complete in more southern races, but there is no abrupt change. The animals formerly intergraded and interbred with their neighbors all the way from Abyssinia down to the Cape. The forms with stripes over most or all of the body are sometimes distinguished as bontequaggas or Burchell's zebras. (Plate Va, and Fig. 3) The most northern forms have rather narrow, numerous, dark and light stripes over the entire body and down the legs to the hoofs. In more southern races the leg striping is weak or absent and the body stripes wider, often with faint 'shadow' stripes between the dark bands. The most southern race, now extinct, had only the head and neck clearly striped. (Plate Vb) The striping was irregular and less distinct on the forequarters and absent on the hindquarters and legs. These animals, the true or typical quaggas of the early Boer settlers, once swarmed on the plains of Cape Colony, but here the old story of human persecution and lack of foresight has run its whole course. The last of these half-striped zebras was killed some time around 1880. Another race intermediate between this and the fully striped bontequaggas has also been killed off by the Boers, but the central African bontequaggas are still numerous and in no immediate danger of extinction.

The mountain zebra, *Equus zebra* (Plate Vc, and Fig. 3), also had the misfortune to live in South Africa, exposed to the skill of the

Boer hunters. It still survives but is very rare and there is some question whether it can indefinitely be saved from extinction. It is even more fully striped than the bontequagga and has a peculiar 'gridiron' of short, transverse stripes on the hindquarters between the hips.

The third species of zebra (as the species are here listed) is *Equus grévyi,* called Grévy's zebra. (Plate Vd, and Fig. 3) It lives in the region of Abyssinia and Somaliland. It is also almost fully striped, with particularly numerous and narrow stripes, but lacks the gridiron of *E. zebra.* In general build *E. grevyi* is the most horse-like of the zebras and might pass as a horse if the stripes were painted out.

It is clear that the living Equidae are all quite clearly related to each other, a fact indicated technically by placing all in one genus, *Equus.* Most of their differences are slight matters of size and proportion without any really definite structural distinctions. *Equus hemionus* almost equally resembles *E. caballus* and *E. asinus. Equus quagga* was more or less intermediate in appearance between *E. zebra* and *E. asinus.* The different sorts of zebras almost intergrade in their variations. Crosses between the various species produce living young, which is only possible with closely related animals. The distinct groups named here have not interbred in nature, however, and the crosses produced by captive or tame animals are usually sterile—the offspring cannot, as a rule, produce young themselves. The mule, a cross between domestic *E. asinus* and *E. caballus,* almost always sterile, is a familiar example. This shows that, although closely related, the six main groups of living Equidae are distinct, natural species.

The most obvious difference between living Equidae is in coloration. A heavily striped *Equus zebra,* for instance, and a self-colored *E. caballus* (a self-colored animal is one without spots, color patches, or stripes) certainly do not look as if they were closely related, but appearances are deceiving. Color patterns are often so variable and they may change so easily in evolution that they are among the least reliable indications of natural relationships. As another example, the striped tiger and the self-colored lion are very closely related; they interbreed freely in captivity and are exceedingly difficult to tell

apart except by their skins. In the case of the horses there are intermediates too: the extinct Cape race of *E. quagga* was half striped
and half not, *E. asinus* is often slightly striped, and even some domestic representatives of *E. caballus* have traces of stripes.

This matter of striping has another interesting aspect. Skin of ancient fossil horses has never been found and the restorations are
based on skeletons only, which give no indication of hair color or
pattern. Artists usually make the restorations self-colored, probably
because they think of the commonly self-colored *Equus caballus* as
the typical or true modern representative of the family. But we have
now seen that most of the living species are more or less striped, and
the more striped species are, on the whole, more primitive than
E. caballus. It is possible that many of the fossil horses were striped,
or even that this was characteristic of the family at one time and
that our horse has simply lost its stripes. Perhaps instead of thinking
of zebras as striped horses we should think of horses as stripeless
zebras.

4

HORSES AND HISTORY

MEN and horses evolved together, but it was a long time before they meant anything to each other. When eohippus roamed the earth, our ancestors were long-tailed lemuroids living in trees and eating fruits and seeds and whatever small vermin came their way. If they noticed eohippus at all, their incoherent reaction could doubtless be translated as, 'You go your way and I'll go mine.' When man finally got down out of the trees, walked about on his hind legs, and began to make tools and to hunt game for food, there was *Equus,* still wholly untamed but a good, full-grown, one-toed horse. *Equus* undoubtedly eyed strange and clumsy *Homo* with apprehension, and this apprehension was well-justified because to *Homo, Equus* looked like food. The association of man and horse had begun, but in a way not too pleasant for the horse.

At Solutré in France there is a great pile of rubbish where Stone Age cave men, who had no garbage service and did not mind smells, threw the remains of their meals. This pile contains thousands of horse bones and is an impressive testimony to the taste of cave men for the dish now sometimes called 'filet of filly.' (This dish is, in fact, excellent, as I have just confirmed during a visit to Harvard University, where horse steak is regularly served at the faculty club.) Many ancient sites besides Solutré add evidence that to prehistoric man the only good horse was a dead horse. Portraits of horses are common in cave paintings by Stone Age men. (Plate VIa). Perhaps some of these horse-eaters raised horses for the table, and the horse may have been domesticated first as a meat animal, but there is no good evidence for this conjecture and it is not likely.

Anyone who started raising horses would almost certainly discover forthwith that, good as horse meat is, the living animal is also useful.

The first men to tame horses and to raise them in domestication could not write and were probably nomads who have left little record of their lives and customs. There is no record of this extremely important event, but from indirect evidence we do have a rough idea when and where it occurred. Definite historical records of domestic horses began as soon as these animals became known to civilized men, and this occurred at almost the same time, not long before 2000 B.C., at opposite ends of Asia, in Mesopotamia and in China. In both cases, the domestic horse or the idea of domestication was introduced by barbarians who had acquired horses some time earlier, but it is not likely that domestication started very much earlier. Perhaps, in view of the poor communications of the time, a few centuries can be allowed and this event placed in more or less 2500 B.C. at a guess.

Domesticating horses must have been easy. All that was necessary was to catch a few wild colts, raise them as tame animals, and in due course let them breed among themselves. Men already had domestic dogs, and I suspect that the unknown hero who first domesticated the horse was really a small boy who wanted a pet. Very likely he was scolded by his father for playing around with that worthless animal. Father little realized that the small boy was one of the greatest innovators in human history. This is just romancing, of course, but it makes the point that although it took a long time to get the idea of domesticating the horse, the idea was a simple one to carry out once someone had it. It is the old story of Columbus and the egg.

Because the idea was such a good one and so simple, it seems probable that it spread rapidly and that no very long time elapsed, as such things went in days when history was more leisurely, before domestication was going on wherever men and wild horses were in contact. This was an enormous area, including most of Europe, a broad strip right across central Asia to the edge of China, and probably also a part of Africa. It is not, then, too surprising that domestic horses first bob up in history at places as distant from each other as Mesopotamia and China. Some historians talk as if just one local race of wild horse were domesticated in just one place and as if the whole story were one of spread of horses from this (unknown) spot, while others speak of two original domestications, and a few think they can distinguish up to six.

A common-sense view of the probable situation when horses were being domesticated suggests that this really took place over a vast region and with a variety of different wild races. These races belonged to a single species and all interbred and graded into each other, so that you could call them all one (*Equus caballus*), or could, if all were known, count them as from two to perhaps a hundred or more local forms. Moreover the domesticated local forms were interbred from very early times, and it was not long before the types or (roughly) breeds established by man were such mixtures and recombinations of the original wild stocks that the idea of derivation of each main domestic type from a particular, natural wild population may be unrealistic or meaningless. I should warn you, however, that this is not the most usual opinion: most students of horse breeds try to interpret them in terms of a few original breeds or wild stocks, species or subspecies. (Two or three is the most popular number.) To me this seems like an unjustified oversimplification.

If my view is correct, then the most important part of the early history of the domestic horse went on behind the scenes, up in Europe and across Asia among tribes that left no records. This does not, however, lessen the importance of the horses introduced into the regions where people could read and write and where horse history and human history soon became intermingled. Of such regions, the Near East, cradle of European civilization, is most interesting to us, and it has been noted that domestic horses appeared here, probably first in Mesopotamia, around 2000 B.C. The Near East in general had few wild *Equus caballus,* and over large parts of it none. For a time all the domestic horses there may have been brought down from the north. It has been surmised that they were first introduced from southeastern Europe, the region north of the Black Sea and the Caspian, either straight south through the Caucasus or south and then west across what is now Iran. It has also been surmised that the first horsemen in this region were the early Indo-European or so-called Aryans—a name that does not properly apply to any particular race, but to diverse groups of ancient wanderers who spoke ancestral languages from which most European and some south Asiatic languages have been derived.

It was several hundred years before horses were well established throughout the Near East. (Portraits of some ancient Near Eastern horses are shown in Plate VIb, c.) Remember that wild horses were uncommon in this region and that, on the whole, it was and is poor country for horses. The earliest records in Greece are dated about 1700 B.C. and in Egypt about 1600 B.C. By 1000 B.C. (and possibly well before this), the use of horses had reached Spain and there are records in India as early as 1500 B.C. About 3000 years ago domestic horses had already been developed or introduced in almost every part of Europe, Asia, and North Africa where the use of horses is at all practical, that is, very roughly, throughout the Temperate Zone of those continents.

Once horses had ceased to be merely food or pets, they became a profound influence on the history of mankind. Even in America today, when the horse is no longer essential to most of us, it continues to be a characteristic and integral part of our culture and to have more economic importance than might be expected in the atomic age. In other times and other cultures the whole social and economic organization has revolved around the horse.

The most obvious influence of horses on history has been in warfare. Horses have been involved in almost every war since war began, and they made possible most of the great conquests before the machine age. Only in recent times has the development of military horses ceased to be the main concern of breeders. Among many ancient nations the horse was solely an instrument of war. At first, horses usually pulled war chariots and this is how they are commonly shown in the sculptures and paintings of ancient Egypt and the other old Near Eastern civilizations. A chariot corps finally proved, however, a poor match for well-trained cavalry, and as larger, more effective riding horses were developed the use of chariots declined.

The Mohammedan and Mongolian conquests, so widespread and characteristic of these brutal events, were powered and made possible by horses. In the early part of the seventh century, Mohammed preached the One God and holy warfare. He also preached horses. Arabian maxims tell the horseman that 'Every grain of barley given to a horse is entered by God in the Register of Good Works,' and assure the horse that 'Thy back shall be a seat of honor and thy belly of riches.' The Arabs mounted their horses, still considered by many horsemen as the best that men have ever bred, and set off to conquer the world.

What finally stopped the Mohammedans and their horses were more horses. Everything had been swept before them, across North Africa and up through Spain into what is now France, when the show-down finally came at Poictiers in A.D. 732. The Mohammedans, mounted on light, swift Arabians and Barbs, there ran head-on into the Franks, clad in mail armor and mounted on heavy European horses. The lighter cavalry could not penetrate the front of these great battle horses, and the Mohammedan thrust into northern Europe was turned back, never to be renewed.

The conquests of the horsemen of Chingis (or Genghis Khan) in the thirteenth century were even more far-flung and were never really turned back. The empire stopped expanding and finally fell apart simply because it became too unwieldy, its lines of communication too long to hold the state together even with the aid of swift horses. The whole Mongolian horde was horse-borne and its leaders developed irresistible cavalry tactics, which have been studied by military experts ever since and have even been taken over into modern mechanized warfare.

The Mongols typified a people who not only owed their success in war to the horse but also had horses as the most essential feature of their whole culture. To a Mongol, life without a horse was impossible. The horse was weapon, buckler, food, drink, friend, and god. Mare's milk was the common drink, fresh or lightly fermented into kumys. From it came too the powerful arak, strong intoxicant of Mongolian drinking bouts. Soldiers traveling without rations sometimes opened one of their horse's veins, drank blood, closed the wound, and remounted. Horse skulls were objects of worship, and horse shoulder blades were used to tell fortunes. Horses were valued as highly as humans—sometimes higher. A horse thief was required to repay nine horses for one, or to give his own children in place of these animals, or to forfeit his life. Forty maidens and forty white horses were said to have been slaughtered on the grave of Chingis. The legend may not be true, but the fact that the Mongolian chroniclers believed it shows their judgment of the relative value of horses and maidens: a compliment to both.

Even from ancient times, and increasingly in more recent days, horses have had historical social and economic roles other than in warfare. They have also served, and still do, as means of peaceful transportation; as a source of power; for recreation, sports, and gambling; as means and emblems of rank, wealth, and authority; for esthetic pleasure; for food (alive and dead); and, after death, not only for food but also for leather and various other products.

Horse cultures, like those of the Mongols, of our plains Indians in wild western days, and, in less intense form, of the western white ranchers celebrated in the 'horse operas' of the movies, depended on two conditions: an abundance of horses and a mobile way of life based on raiding, hunting, or herding. Where horses were few, they had to be confined to the wealthy or reserved for the most important business, which was usually warfare. This has generally been true in the Mediterranean area, cradle of the civilizations best known to us. The work animals there were usually donkeys, sometimes camels, seldom horses, and this is still true today. The man with a horse was an aristocrat or a fighter. Even in northern and western Europe, a commoner seldom rode a horse or was pulled by one until the last century or two before the coming of the automobile.

The use of horses as a usual source of power, on farms or in industry, was probably older in northern Europe than elsewhere, but even here it was not usual until rather late in history and in restricted areas with relatively high living standards. In most times and places, the movement of goods, the plowing of fields, the raising of water, and other power operations have usually been performed by humbler and cheaper animals: by donkeys, mules, or oxen, or by the humblest work animal of all, the human slave or serf.

Horses seem to have been most appreciated where they were of least economic importance. The Greeks were not great horsemen in war or peace and had no particular dependence on the work of horses, but they raised esthetic appreciation of these animals to a pitch never surpassed. The horses of the Parthenon frieze and of many lesser, but also beautiful, Greek works of art are surely among the finest things ever made by the hand of man. (See Plate VIc, d) The Greeks were also addicted to horse racing. At Olympia, beginning as far as we know in 648 B.C., there were chariot races, mounted horse races, and even mule-car races. Among the Romans, chariot racing was one of the most popular professional sports. The four racing factions, each with its own colors, spent enormous sums on the races, and the successful drivers were as popular and well-known as any heavyweight boxing champion of today.

We owe to the Roman historian Pliny a story which, even if we read it with tongue in cheek, suggests that the use of horses for pure amusement is also ancient. The tale goes that the Sybarites, whose name has become synonymous with luxury, trained their horses to dance to music at banquets. Their enemies, the Crotonians, attacked the Sybarites, who mounted their horses and sallied out to fight. Thereupon the wily Crotonians played dance music, the horses danced, the Sybarites were thrown, and the Crotonians won the battle. Moral: Do your own dancing and let the horse watch you.

The horse as luxury or entertainment is well enough exemplified by the dancing horses of the Sybarites or of the modern circus, but perhaps reaches its acme in the hunt. Starting as a hard means of earning a living, hunting on horseback has wound up as an ideal symbol of a privileged class: it is difficult, dangerous, exhilarating, expensive, and useless. Horse-racing, in spite of its claim to be the sport of kings, has become a gambling device for the man in the street, but hunting remains as a purely aristocratic occupation, in the best sense of the now rather unpopular word 'aristocratic.'

Aside from hunting, the horse in western civilization has also been from ancient times among the trappings and symbols of aristocracy.

In old Athens, under Solon's Constitution, the *hippeis,* men who owned at least one horse each, were legally recognized as a special upper class of the citizenry. The European languages testify to the long tradition that anyone who has a horse is a socially superior being: 'cavalier' in English, 'chevalier' in French, 'caballero' in Spanish, 'Ritter' in German—all these and other designations of aristocrats originally meant simply 'a horseman.' It is a long tradition of prestige and authority that is inherited by our mounted policemen.

These are some of the many ways in which the histories of horse-kind and of mankind have been intertwined throughout much of the world in the past. What of the horse in America today and tomorrow?

From the time of their introduction in early colonial days up to 1918, the number of horses in the United States increased steadily. In 1918, the peak year, there were over 21 million horses on farms in this country. Since then, there has been a rapid drop. In 1947 the U.S. Department of Agriculture estimated that there were about 7,250,000 horses and about 2,750,000 mules on farms. There were probably another half-million horses or so not on farms: race horses, pleasure horses, work horses in lumber camps, road construction, mines, et cetera. In all, the number of horses has dropped in thirty years to decidedly less than half the peak figure.

This is just what everyone would expect. 'The day of the horse is done.' Automobile production passed the million per year mark at just about the time when the horse population began its rapid decline, and that was no coincidence.

But seven or eight million horses are still a lot of horses. Horses are not really uncommon in the United States today, and there is no reason to think that the decrease will go on indefinitely until it reaches zero. It would be safer to predict that the association of horse and man that began four or five thousand years ago will go on as long as man does. Ours is the most mechanized of countries, but we still find use for millions of horses. In many countries horses are still the main source of rural power and an essential means of transportation. Tractors and automobiles will inevitably displace

horses for these purposes almost everywhere in time, but there will
long remain farms where horses are more efficient than machines, out
of the way places where they are still the fastest means of travel, and
cattle ranges where the stock can be more easily handled with
horses than in any other way.

Horses as work animals will probably continue long after our
generation, but sometime, it is true, the day may come when the last
work horse is turned out to pasture. Horses as implements of war
are already through, after a long and bloody history. They were
used extensively, sometimes even decisively, in the First World War.
Some were used in the Second World War, but their role was then
relatively unimportant in spite of the anguish of some die-hard
cavalrymen. It is highly improbable that horses will be a decisive
factor in any future war.

The future doubtless belongs to the race horse and the pleasure
horse, and their prospect looks rosy. Only the most world-wide,
disastrous poverty could seriously threaten this future, and even then
horses would probably be kept somehow. Mechanized racing has not
replaced or even visibly affected the tremendous interest in horse
racing. Riding for recreation is probably more popular than ever
before and certainly reaches a wider cross-section of the population.
It is no longer confined to the few who can afford the luxury of
maintaining park hacks or hunters, but is inexpensively available
to anyone who can afford a brief vacation. There are 'western' dude
ranches within the shadow of New York City. Many colleges and
some schools teach riding and maintain stables for their students.
Rodeos are increasingly numerous and popular, and horses continue
to be indispensable in circuses.

In view of the profound changes that occurred in the evolution
of the horse, it is natural to ask whether horses may not continue to
evolve and change into something quite different in the future. I
predict that they will not—this is perfectly safe, because even if horses
do evolve into radically new forms, this will be so long in the future
that no one will read or remember the prediction. Horses have not
changed really to amount to much in the last million years, and
who can say that man himself will last another million? Furthermore,

it is hard to see how or why any appreciable change should occur no matter how long horses and men continue. Our horse has one toe on each foot; the number cannot be reduced. He is adequately specialized for a widely available sort of food; a marked change in teeth and digestive system would be unnecessary and probably impracticable. He is about as fast as is mechanically possible for an animal also capable of carrying a man on its back; any radical change in general build and limbs would be disadvantageous to man and would be countered by selective breeding. The horse is both intelligent enough and stupid enough to do what we demand of him.

As the work horse disappears, man will probably lose interest in some of the more special and particularly the heavier breeds and may permit them to die out. There may well be a reduction in variety, except as odd types might be retained from curiosity and for show. Most of the horses of the distant future will probably be of only two main types: specialized racers similar to or identical with our Thoroughbreds, and horses similar to our Saddlers and related breeds, probably bred in a variety of sizes to fit young and adult, light and heavy riders. A demand for work horses, especially on farms, still exists at present and will continue for some time, but even in this field there is already an evident trend toward a more medium, general utility type, standing 16 hands or less and weighing 1500 pounds or less.

5

ANCIENT BREEDS

THE first horses that were brought down (it is supposed) from north of the Caucasus into the light of history seem to have been rather small, stocky animals. It was probably because of their small size that in the earlier part of their history domestic horses in the ancient Near East were more commonly used to pull chariots than for riding. Before long the Egyptians were active horse-traders and were involved, both directly and as middlemen, in cross-breeding of the light but rather stocky, usually pale-colored horses from the north with more fleet and slender, usually dark-colored horses. Some, at least, of these seem to have come from the west, that is, from the Libyans or Numidians of North Africa.

And just here, toward the beginning of the story, appears one of the most mysterious and disputed points affecting the origin of modern breeds. According to one theory, probably the most popular at present, all the light, fast Mediterranean and Near Eastern horses were from a single original stock, represented today in purest form by the Arabian horse. If this is true, then the ancient Numidian horses, which now are represented (evidently in much modified form) by the Barbs, were of common origin with the Arabian horses. The most widely held theory accepts this view and supposes that Near Eastern horses, more or less of Arabian type, had early been introduced into northwestern Africa and there developed into the Numidian horses. Another opinion accepts the common origin of the two, but supposes that the Arabian horse developed from Numidian horses introduced from Africa into the Near East. The fact seems to be that the Numidian horse appears earlier in recorded history than the true Arabian, although horses more or less of Arabian type are among the oldest in the Near East (but probably not in Arabia).

It is also true that the Barb and Arabian of today, and as far back as we can definitely recognize the types, are distinct. (Barbs are so named from Barbary, an old name for North Africa west of Egypt.) They are both light, fast horses, but the typical Barb lacks the special peculiarities of the Arab, such as the wedge-shaped head, dished profile, protruding eyes, et cetera. On this account still other authorities refuse to consider Barb and Arab as local breeds of the same original stock and insist that their ancestry was quite different, with the Barb going back, perhaps, to a European origin in coarser, less-spirited horses such as are called 'cold-blooded' by breeders. To complicate matters still more, the best modern North African horses, geographically Barbs, often have considerable Arabian blood and it has been claimed that some 'Barbs' were in fact pure Arabians that happened to have been bred in Barbary. It may also be pointed out that most of the horses shown in ancient Egyptian and Greek art do not look quite like either Barbs or Arabs.

Without taking sides in this controversy, we may refer to the previous surmise that the earliest domestic horses probably did not belong to any one, two, or other small and definite number of distinct and recognizable breeds. At any rate, in early times and right down through history to the present day, there were always many local types of horses and these local types were constantly being interbred and modified. As a matter of description, the typical Mediterranean and Near Eastern horses, from the most ancient times to the present, have usually been slender, fast, and rather small (but generally above pony size). This would doubtless be true wherever the stock originally came from and whether it had one origin or many, because these horses are raised in an environment generally unfavorable to them and their owners have prized speed above weight or power.

Out of this general, light stock the Arabian horse developed and has been retained as one of the most clear-cut and important breeds, probably the oldest breed to be set aside definitely as such and to be

maintained in pure, known blood lines. Not only the origin but also
the antiquity of the breed is disputed. That it has existed and has
been kept without marked change since about the time of Mohammed, in the seventh century, is reasonably established, but before
that much is obscure. Some students maintain that the Arabs had no
horses until Mohammed's day and others that the Arabs had horses
in early prehistoric times and were among the first men to have
them. As is so often the case, the truth probably lies between the two
extremes. It is almost incredible and is supported by no real evidence that Arabia was itself an original center of horse domestication. On the other hand, some of the oldest known representations
of horses from places in Asia not in but near Arabia bear a distinct
resemblance to the Arabian breed. Horses resembling Arabians were
probably among the first to be produced by domestication. It is reasonable to assume that these were the ancestors, or were among the
ancestors, of horses introduced later into Arabia and developed into
the Arabian, strictly speaking, perhaps around the beginning of the
Christian era. There are references to horses in pre-Islamic Arabian poetry that sufficiently indicate that the Arabs knew and had
horses in the last few centuries before the Mohammedan era, which
began in the year 622 of the Christian era.

Horses were probably not numerous in early Arabia and, in fact,
horses are not particularly numerous there today. Recent authorities
estimate that there have been only about 50 thousand horses in all
of Arabia at any one time in the last century or so, the great majority
of these not purebred Arabians. It is indeed inbreeding within a relatively small stock of individually highly prized horses that has kept
this ancient type recognizable and distinct for so long a time.

Wherever they came from originally, the peculiarities of the desert
horses of Arabia have been intensified and maintained by long inbreeding and by selection, natural and human, in an environment
poor for horses and demanding toughness, alertness, and speed in
those that survive. Even in the desert, not all horses are accounted
purebred, *asil*, by the Arabs. The great majority are *kudsh*, impure,
a term sometimes applied to Arabians of faulty pedigree and sometimes to all horses except pure Arabians. (It is impossible to write

Arabic words correctly with our alphabet and many different spellings of these words may be found.) In Arabia, pedigrees are kept through the mares only, and brood mares are valued for pedigree as much as for conformation, or more. The sire of an *asil* foal must, however, be *asil* himself and stallions for breeding may be more carefully selected for style and build than are mares, so that selection in the male line may really be more important than in the female line of pedigree.

Purity of line is so fanatically regarded by the desert Arabs that if a mare has once mated with a *kudsh* stallion, her progeny ever after are *kudsh,* even though their own sires be *asil* of the best. This idea that foals may inherit not only from their actual sires but also from previous mates of their dams is completely false, but it has been traditional not only among the Arabs but also among many European and American breeders. The desert Arabs' ideas of purity in breeding are so rigid that many horses that are, in fact, excellent Arabians and that would be accepted as purebred by our standards are by them despised as *kudsh.*

There is a tradition that there are five strains of *asil* Arabians, called *el khamsa* ('the five'), but authorities do not agree which strains constitute the *khamsa* and in fact about twenty strains of *asil* Arabians are current among the Arabs. The most widespread strain is the Kuhaylan (a name sometimes extended to all *asil* Arabians), with some hundred recognized families or blood lines. The name derives from *kuhl* (the 'h' is not silent), which is the name of the dark paint (commonly antimony) used by Arab women to beautify their eyes. The reason for this odd transfer of the word from eyepaint to purebred horses is that Arabian horses have black skins, the color of *kuhl,* as one of their striking characteristics.

Although their skins should always be dark, the coats of Arabians may be of almost any color. Bay is the usual and most prized color among the Arabs, but a wide variety of colors, from dark brown to white, occur among *asil* or Kuhaylan Arabians. It is a curious fact, true not only of Arabians but also of many white horses of other breeds, that the white horses (not albinos) are born dark gray, sometimes almost black, and fade to white during the following years of their lives. Black, cream or yellow, and isabel or palomino Arabians do occur but they are rare and these colors are usually considered by the Arabs as indicating some impurity of strain. Spotted (parti-colored or pinto) horses are said to be unknown to the Arabs.

The head of the Arabian horse is very distinctive. The prime point, called *jibbah* by the Arabs, is the broad, bulging forehead. The profile is usually concave in front of this swelling, giving the head a characteristic and prized dished appearance. The eyes are large, somewhat protruding, and set lower in the head and relatively nearer the muzzle than is usual in other breeds. The muzzle is delicate and tapering, with long, thin lips. The swollen back of the head and the light muzzle give the head as a whole a wedge-shaped appearance as seen in side view, strikingly different from the blunt heads of more heavy-muzzled, so-called cold-blooded breeds.

The neck is long and has a characteristic arch (*mitbah*) at the top of the crest. The chest is round, large, and powerful. The back is straight and unusually short. It generally has only 23 vertebrae, whereas 24 is the usual number in all other breeds—one of the most extraordinary features of the Arabian. The pelvis is long and is set more nearly horizontally than is common in horses. In comparison with the short back and barrel chest, the legs are unusually long. They are strikingly slender, but are well muscled and the bones are dense and strong.

Such is the horse that many students and horse fanciers consider the very pinnacle of horse evolution. It is certainly one of the most attractive of horses, or of all animals. (See Plate VIIa, b) For centuries Arabians have been exported from Arabia and used in cross-breeding to improve and in some cases to originate non-Arabian breeds. Most of these exports were stallions. The Arabs are more reluctant to part with mares, and foreign breeders have usually preferred to use Arabian stallions and domestic mares. Some Arabian mares have, however, been exported and purebred Arabians (although possibly not always *asil* to an Arab) are now raised in the United States and elsewhere outside Arabia. One of the most famous of these studs, and the source of much of our American Arabian stock, was that of Wilfred and Lady Anne Blunt at Crebbet Park in England, maintained after their death by their daughter Lady Wentworth. An Arabian Horse Club of America was established in 1908, and it maintains a stud book for this breed. Just before World War II the club was registering about 100 Arabians per year.

There are so few purebred Arabians that these beautiful horses might be considered interesting but not particularly important were it not for the fact that their blood flows in the veins of almost all fine horses, and a great many common ones, all over the world. Our running horses, the Thoroughbreds, have partly Arabian ancestry and, through the Thoroughbreds or more directly, part of the Arabian inheritance has been introduced into most other breeds. This process has been going on for many centuries.

When the Arabs set out on conquest, they increased their cavalry stock by appropriating local horses wherever they went. They did not, as a rule, take back foreign horses and mingle them with the highly valued purebred lines in Arabia, but their horses crossed with all those encountered outside Arabia. Thus more or less Arabian blood was introduced throughout North Africa and as far as Spain, and in the other direction throughout the Near East and as far as India. This again, like the earlier trading and breeding activities of the Egyptians and their neighbors, helped to promote a general Mediterranean-Near Eastern type of light, fast, hot-blooded, so-called 'desert' horse, in spite of many local differences in minor type and the possibly mixed origin of the group as a whole.

In Spain a horse of this general sort, but somewhat coarser than some of the other local types, developed with large admixture of Barb and perhaps some Arab from Africa and some mixture also with 'cold' blood from north of the Pyrenees. This horse, the jineta or jennet, although not established and carried down to us as a pure breed, was once popular in England and contributed blood to the English saddle horses. (Shakespeare recorded an incident of this crossing, in the flirtation of the jennet of Venus with the courser of Adonis.) The greatest interest of the Spanish horses to us is, however, that they were brought to the New World by the conquistadores, explorers, and early colonists and, escaping in our western plains and on the pampas, became the 'wild' (that is, feral) horses of our west and of Argentina. The mustang had a hard life and preserved little of the proud bearing of the jineta, but he was extraordinarily tough and alert. From him, with admixture from other sources, came the ponies of the Indians, and his blood, now much diffused with more civilized strains, flows in the western cowponies and in many other American horses.

While the Arab, the Barb, the jineta, and other less characteristic types of horses were being developed around the Mediterranean, domestic horses had also become common in Europe north of the Alps and the Pyrenees. Among these, besides nondescript types and intermediates in a population without complete segregation of breeds, two sorts were outstanding: the light but strong European or Celtic pony and the large, heavy, cold-blooded horse. Both these appear at prehistoric sites of several centuries B.C. and both survive today in modified form.

The typical Celtic pony was only 11 to 12 hands in height. (A 'hand,' usual measurement of height in domestic horses, is 4 inches. Height is measured from the ground to the top of the withers; 12:2 or 12.2 hands, for instance, means 12 hands 2 inches and is equivalent to 50 inches, or 4'2" height at the shoulders.) The Celtic pony was well-formed and light in weight, but sturdy and rather short-legged. The head was small, relatively short-faced, and broad and rounded behind the eyes. It was literally a light (weight) horse and those who consider all domestic horses as coming from one light and one heavy original stock suppose that it came from the 'light' stock along with the Arab and other Oriental types. Another and more reasonable possibility is that its ancestors were the relatively small variants or local races within Europe of the general interbreeding Eurasian wild-horse species. In any case, its most nearly pure descendants are quite unlike either Arabs or Barbs, which are also considered of light stock. The Iceland pony (Plate VIIc) is among the less modified descendants of the Celtic pony.

From the heavier prehistoric horses, the Great Horse of the Middle Ages was developed. (Plate VIIIb) This was a very large, rather slow but powerful horse, a typical 'cold-blood' in breeder's parlance, often standing over 16 hands. It was developed particularly as a military horse, and its strength was needed in order to carry a heavily armed knight. There were several distinctive local types, with, of course, much interbreeding. Among others, a continental or Flemish type and a British type could be distinguished.

6

SOME EUROPEAN BREEDS IN AMERICA

NO two horses are precisely alike, any more than any two men are ever really complete doubles. Each horse has its own peculiarities of color, of conformation (that is, of general build, size, shape, and proportions), and of performance, which add up to an individual personality. Nevertheless, horses do resemble each other, some more and some less. All those that are similar by some standard or definition of conformation and performance are spoken of as belonging to a given type. By careful selection of type for breeding purposes and then by inbreeding among the offspring of the desired type, it is often (although not always) possible to fix the wanted characteristics and to produce a stock of related animals that breed true to type. Typical conformation and performance then become fixed in heredity and appear in all the offspring as long as breeding is confined to established family lines of the type. Such a stock of interrelated, true-breeding animals constitutes a breed.

Many breeds, among horses and other animals, have arisen in an informal way. Types desirable in a particular region and for particular purposes were preferred and were fixed by inbreeding more or less automatically because each breeder bred from his own animals or the similar and related animals of his near neighbors. Particularly good local breeds tended to be more consciously preserved by traditional methods and by maintenance of unwritten pedigrees, as among the Arabs. More recently, new breeds have been consciously developed and older breeds have been maintained, standardized, or modified by a system of written registration. An association for promoting or establishing a given breed registers animals that meet its standards of conformation and performance, assigns a number to each, keeps track of their breeding, and usually publishes a list of registered horses of the breed in a stud book. As a final step, registration is closed, that is, no foal will be accepted and registered as belonging to the breed unless both sire and dam were registered in the same breed.

Nowadays in the United States and most other countries, no horse can properly be represented as a purebred representative of a breed unless it is registered or, at least, is eligible for registry. Crosses between purebred and unregistered lines are called grades. Repeated crossing into a given breed may produce grade horses that are indistinguishable from their purebred relatives, even by an expert, except by the record. Most grades naturally differ more or less from purebred horses and are more varied in type. At least nine-tenths of the horses on American farms are grades or 'just plain horse,' of unknown ancestry. The maintenance of the relatively smaller purebred stocks is desirable and important not only for the usefulness of these aristocrats themselves, but also for their value in producing grades that improve the quality of the general stock of cheaper horses and in cross-breeding for types desirable for some special purpose.

There are perhaps sixty recognized breeds of horses in the world today. Among dogs, which are older as domestic animals and much more variable, there are probably at least two hundred breeds, and the differences between some of these are far greater than between the most extreme breeds of horses. About one-fourth of the known breeds of horses are regularly bred or registered in the United States. These include practically the whole range of size and other characteristics found in all breeds and give a good idea of the different types of domestic horses in general. They are also the breeds familiar and accessible to most readers of this book. Discussion of breeds here will therefore be confined to those of American registry, with some notice also of a few other American horses that cannot, for one reason or another, be considered as true breeds.

The immediate ancestors of all modern American horses came from the Old World, mainly from Europe. Some distinctive American types and breeds have been developed since horses were brought over here: these will be discussed in following chapters. Most of our breeds originated as such in Europe, but separate American registry has nevertheless made them thoroughly American horses. Some importations from Europe have been made in recent years, but in most cases it is generations since there has been much crossing of American lines with European horses of the same breeds.

Among the most characteristic of breeds that originated in Europe and are now extensively bred in America are the various heavy draft horses. These were all derived from the northwestern European Great Horses of the Middle Ages. With the passing of chivalry and the replacement of armored knights by light cavalry, these heavy horses were demoted to pulling coaches and wagons. Their descendants persist today in lines somewhat refined by infusion of some light horse blood by outcrossing with Oriental and related types. The most popular of these horses in America are the Belgian and the Percheron, which have been about equally numerous here, although in recent years the Belgian seems to have gained slightly over the formerly favored Percheron. In 1947, 618 Belgians and 449 Percherons were registered in the United States. There are perhaps forty or fifty thousand purebred horses of these two breeds now living here.

The Percheron (Plate IXa) originated in the district of La Perche in France and was first imported into the United States in 1839. Its forebears in the seventeenth and eighteenth centuries were smaller than the present Percheron and were used as general-purpose horses, sometimes even as hunters. The Percheron remains remarkably agile for its size, which now is commonly between 16 and 17 hands in height and around a ton in weight. The strength is tremendous and is reflected in the generally low-down and thick-set conformation, with a short back and heavy lower thigh muscles. The head is of medium size, sometimes appearing small for so large an animal, broad between the eyes, and with lean, clean lines. There is some feather (long hair above the fetlock). Most Percherons are dapple gray, but black is also common and equally desirable.

The Belgian (Plate IXb) has also been developed from the continental type of Great Horse and is the modern representative of the

Flemish Horse, a very ancient type in regions now included in Belgium. It has been bred in the United States since 1866. The old Flemish Horse was black, but Belgians are now usually sorrel, chestnut, bay, or red roan, although an occasional purebred Belgian is black or gray. (Some remarks on the colors of horses are given in chapter 9: 'A Horse of Another Color.') Except for the predominance of chestnut and bay, which is probably a reason for the increasing popularity of the breed, Belgians are closely similar to Percherons in conformation and performance, and they have much the same virtues.

Both Percherons and Belgians have often been crossed with somewhat smaller horses to produce lighter, high-class draft and utility-grade horses. The experiment has no practical value, but it is interesting and it demonstrates the close relationship of all domestic horses to note that Percherons have been successfully crossed with the diminutive Shetlands.

England has provided us with three draft breeds, the Shire, Clydesdale, and Suffolk, which are not as common as the Percheron and Belgian in the United States but each of which has its ardent supporters here.

The Shire was developed from the English Great Horse as a farm draft horse and for heavy carting. As with the Belgian horse, its ancestors were mainly black, but brown, bay, and sorrel are now more common and chestnut, roan, and gray also occur. This is the largest of our breeds, the stallions often exceeding 17 hands in height and weighing upwards of 2200 pounds. It averages bigger all around than our other draft horses and is heavily feathered. Shires have excellent reputations for docility and working capacity. That they are not more common is doubtless due to the fact that they are really too large and powerful for most modern uses.

The Clydesdale (Plate IXc), which ranks in popularity next after the Belgian and Percheron among our heavy draft breeds, originated around the River Clyde in Scotland during the eighteenth century. It is slightly smaller than the three breeds just discussed, stallions averaging little over 16 hands in height and about 1800 pounds in weight. The ancestral dark color has been retained, although brown and brown-bay may occur, as well as black. The feather is heavy, more or less as in the Shire. Clydesdale breeders point with special pride to its high, free action, which, with the flowing hair at the fetlocks, gives it an especially smart and picturesque appearance in the show ring. It is, however, by no means merely a show animal but is a useful agricultural power plant.

The Suffolk (Plate IXd) is the smallest of the breeds properly called heavy draft horses and is probably the least common in this country, although it has its particular excellent qualities. It averages about 16 hands in height and usually runs between 1500 and 1600 pounds. The conformation is distinctive in being remarkably compact, with short, thick neck, short back and legs, rotund throughout. This conformation, described as 'punched up,' gave the breed its older name of 'Suffolk Punch.' It is an ancient type in England, where it originated in and around Suffolk, and it has probably been outcrossed less than the other heavy breeds. An incidental result of this purity of strain has been that the color has become fixed and is always chestnut, although the exact shade may vary from dark liver to golden sorrel. Pound for pound, there is perhaps no more powerful or stouthearted pulling horse. It is essentially a farm breed.

As time went on, the demand in England for extremely powerful horses to pull heavy loads over bad roads became less. There was increasing need for lighter, but still strong, horses for pulling carriages and for general utility. Draft horses were bred for smaller size and were crossed with Thoroughbred and other light, fast horses. This was the origin of the Cleveland Bay and the Hackney, both of which were long since introduced into America from England but which are not now numerous in this country.

The Cleveland Bay (Plate Xa) is an intermediate type, heavy enough for much draft work but light and fast enough for riding. Its enthusiasts claim that it is the only pure breed of general utility horse. It arose in the Cleveland district, Yorkshire, and is related to the old 'Chapman horse' of that region, with some infusion of racing stock. It was perhaps from horses of this general type that the Thoroughbred was developed by crossing with Oriental horses. However that may be, the Cleveland Bay of today does look something like a rugged, compact Thoroughbred, with deeper girth, shorter legs, and larger knees and hocks. As the name indicates, these horses are always solid bay in color, and they lack white markings. The average height is just under 16 hands and the weight about 1400 or 1450 pounds.

The Hackneys imported from England were the fancy, high-stepping carriage horses of the more sporty and prosperous among our grandfathers, competing in this field with our native Morgans and Standard Breds. In the heyday of the carriage, Hackneys were around 15 hands in height and 1000 pounds in weight. Their former function has been taken over by sports model motor cars, and the modern Hackney (Plate Xb) survives almost exclusively as a diminutive show horse, really a pony and weighing as little as 700 pounds. The smart appearance of the little horses and the exaggeratedly high action of their trot makes them an attractive spectacle in the ring, but most of the present purebred Hackneys are too nervous and spirited to be popular outside of shows. (The change in type that has taken place in this breed in a relatively short time suggests that students should be more cautious in concluding that modern horses of particular types represent descent from early historic or prehistoric races of similar types.)

At the opposite end of the scale from the great Percherons or Shires are the diminutive ponies derived, in the main, from the Celtic pony of early times, with, in some cases, considerable admixture of Thoroughbred and other blood. In Great Britain eight native breeds and one (Connemara) from Ireland are commonly recognized. Individuals of a number of these breeds have been imported into the United States from time to time, but only two, the Welsh and, in greater numbers, the Shetland pony, have been commonly bred here.

Welsh ponies (Plate Xc) may reach 13 hands or even a little more, but 12 hands or less is a common and generally preferred height. The weight is about 500 pounds or less. The small head has large eyes and usually a slightly dished profile. The body is that of a desirable type of small and short-legged saddle horse. The color is not fixed and may be almost anything, black, gray, bay, chestnut, white, but not spotted. The larger Welsh ponies can carry adult riders and some of them are outstanding jumpers. Their character as small horses, more than ponies in the usual understanding of the word, seems to derive in part from the fact that a Thoroughbred stallion was turned in with the droves of pony mares in Wales about 1825.

The development of the Hackney from a carriage horse to a harness pony has been brought about in part by outcrosses with Welsh ponies. In recent years a type (not breed) designated as 'Harness Show Pony' has been developed and registered in America. It is a cross of Welsh stallions with Shetland mares. (Shetland on Hackney crosses are also shown.)

The Shetland pony is our smallest horse. The breed standards allow heights up to 10:2 hands, but a height of 10 hands is more common and many Shetlands stand under 9 hands. This tiny horse originated in the bleak Shetland Islands, north of Scotland and in the latitude of central Norway. They exemplify the fact that small races tend to develop where pasturage is limited and crowded, as is often true on islands. This is not because of direct stunting of the animals by lack of food: Shetlands remain small no matter how well fed. It is because the smaller animals can live on less and are more likely to survive and to breed in times of shortage. The smaller animals in each generation are thus favored by natural selection and sometimes consciously by breeders under these conditions, and the whole race tends to become smaller in time.

In their original home, the Shetlands were draft animals in spite of their small size, and in England, where they were imported and used in the coal pits, the ideal was 'as much weight and as near the ground as possible.' The English still favor a Shetland type that is strong and rather heavy-set. American Shetlands are used as mounts for small children and a more slender, more saddle-horse-like type is favored. Almost all colors occur, although chestnuts are less common than black, brown, bay, or white. Spotted (pinto) ponies are not excluded, as they are in most other registered true breeds, but on the contrary may be sought after for their appeal to children and for use in circuses.

Last of the European breeds to be discussed here, but very far from least in numbers or in the estimation of its millions of followers, is the Thoroughbred. (Plate Xd) Probably no reader of this book needs to be told that Thoroughbred is the name of a very definite breed, not a synonym for 'purebred,' that the Thoroughbred is the running race horse, and that all running horses at recognized meetings are required to be registered Thoroughbreds. (This is not to say that many a fine race is not run by other types of horses at meetings outside the ken of the Jockey Club, for instance the Quarter Horse races popular in the southwest.) An *American Stud Book* appeared in 1834 and the present official *Stud Book* of the Jockey Club began publication in 1868.

The Thoroughbred originated in England and is conventionally traced to the mating of English racing mares of unknown ancestry with three Oriental stallions. Thoroughbreds are all descendants of these three imported stallions: The Byerley Turk, imported in 1689; the Darley Arabian, shortly after 1700; and the Godolphin Barb, about 1730. A good many other Arabians, Barbs, and Turks had, indeed, been imported and the mares bred with these three celebrated sires undoubtedly already had considerable Oriental blood. All three horses were of rather obscure origin. The Godolphin Barb was found in Paris pulling a water-cart! Its British owner, Lord Godolphin, considered it an Arabian and it is so recorded in some histories, but most recent students believe that it was a Barb, that is, of North African stock with probably some admixture of Arabian but not pure Arabian. The Byerley Turk was probably a similar mixture bred in Turkey. (This is, of course, indignantly denied by some Arabian-fanciers who maintain, against the evidence, that all three of these great sires were pure Arabian.)

The foundation sires of the Thoroughbred breed, that is, the ancestors from whom descent is traced for registration, are three of the early descendants of the imported stallions: Eclipse, Matchem, and Herod. Eclipse, most famous of the foundation sires and one of the great race horses of all time, was foaled in 1764 and was a great-grandson of the Darley Arabian. (There was also an American Eclipse, a descendant of the English Eclipse and a famous horse in his own right, foaled on Long Island in 1823.) Matchem, foaled in 1748, was a grandson of the Godolphin Barb. Herod, least esteemed of the three, was a great-great-grandson of the Byerley Turk. Eclipse,

Matchem, and Herod were related through other lines. All modern
Thoroughbreds are related to each other in complex and multiple
ways.

It seems almost superfluous to describe the Thoroughbred, which
must be familiar to everyone from newsreels, photographs, prints,
and paintings if not in person. There are probably many devotees
of racing who know every point of the Thoroughbred but who never
saw any other kind of horse. For comparison with other breeds, it
may be noted that Thoroughbreds are upstanding horses usually
about 16 hands in height, sometimes as much as 17. Thoroughbreds
of 15 hands, a good size for an Arabian, occur but are considered
small. The color is not fixed but is commonly black, bay, chestnut,
or one of the numerous varieties of these basic colors. Palominos,
pintos, and albinos do not occur, but may be common enough in
some strains of grade Thoroughbreds.

Thoroughbreds have been developed to be running machines,
and every line and point, from the slender nose to the flowing tail,
reflect this purpose. The specialization for the single function of
speed, sustained over moderate distances, has produced great grace
and beauty. The speed attained by these, the fastest of all horses,
may slightly exceed 40 miles per hour for short distances, under a
mile. One of the great racing performances of all time was Equipoise's mile, an American record that stood until 1950, run as a
four-year-old, carrying 128 lbs., at Arlington Park, Illinois, on
30 June 1932. The time for the mile was 1 minute 34⅖ seconds, an
average speed of 38.14 miles per hour. The second quarter was run
at nearly 40 miles per hour (39.47 to be exact), but Equipoise was
tiring toward the end and his speed dropped to about 35 miles per
hour. In 1950 Equipoise's record was finally broken at Golden Gate
Track, California, by 'Big Cy,' Citation. Citation's mile was run in
1 minute 33⅗ seconds at an average speed of 38.46 miles per hour.
Several horses have attained 40 miles per hour for short distances as
parts of longer races. In 1949 in Gulfstream Park, Florida, Coaltown
ran the second quarter of a record-tying mile and a quarter race at
40.18 miles per hour and averaged exactly 40 miles per hour for the

first half mile. There seems to be no authentic racing record involving speed of 41 miles per hour or better.

Even though records may again be beaten by fractions of a second, 41 miles per hour appears to be the approximate limit of physical possibility for a running horse. The fastest official record for human racing at any distance is a little over 22 miles per hour, and it is unlikely that any man has ever run 25 miles per hour even in a short spurt. In average speed for a full mile, no record is quite as high as 15 miles per hour.

Specialized breeding of Thoroughbreds for speed has also had disadvantages or, at least, has failed to promote perfect adaptation to other functions. These horses tend to be delicate, thin-skinned, nervous, and high-strung. No other horses can compete with them for saddle racing and few can equal them for jumping, but for other purposes other types of horses are, as a rule, preferable to them. The importance of the Thoroughbred is not, however, confined to the perfection of that breed itself. Many other fine breeds have been developed from the Thoroughbred or contain much Thoroughbred blood, and most saddle or light-harness horses are improved by the speed and spirit conferred by some degree of crossing with a Thoroughbred strain.

7

AN INTERLUDE ON GAITS AND THE
INVENTION OF MOTION PICTURES

THE invention of motion pictures can be traced to an argument among the ancient Egyptians whether a horse while trotting ever has all four feet off the ground at once. The Egyptians had no way of settling the argument, because the feet of a fast trotter move too rapidly for an observer to be quite sure what he sees. The dispute continued through the ages and in 1872 it was still being carried on by Leland Stanford and some of his friends in California. Until then this question had been treated like the weather: everyone talked about it but no one did anything about it. Leland Stanford and a photographer named Eadweard Muybridge (Plate XIa) decided, at last, to do something about finding out how a horse trots. Muybridge worked on the problem for some time at Stanford's stock farm at Palo Alto and later (in 1884 and 1885) at the University of Pennsylvania. He finally included in his studies not only all the basic gaits of the horse but also gaits of numerous other animals and of men.

Muybridge's method was to take consecutive pictures of moving animals in rapid succession. With the primitive photography of those days, the pictures had to be taken on glass plates wet-coated immediately before use. Each picture had to be taken by a different lens. The final set-up (shown in Plate XIb) had 24 single-lens cameras and two large cameras with 12 lenses each. The correct timing of the exposures was ingeniously accomplished by clockwork and electromagnetic circuits. Muybridge's skill is suggested by the fact that he succeeded in taking exposures as short as $\frac{1}{6000}$ second, and this at a time when an exposure of ½ second was considered 'instantaneous'!

Leland Stanford employed a physician, one J. D. B. Stillman, A.M., M.D., to analyze Muybridge's early pictures, and in 1882 they published a volume with the grandiose title, *The horse in motion as shown by instantaneous photography with a study on animal mechanics founded on anatomy and the revelations of the camera in which is demonstrated the theory of quadrupedal locomotion.* The old question was answered: a trotting horse does have all four feet off the ground twice during each stride. Stillman's discussion is, nevertheless, more noteworthy for its piety than for its scientific accuracy. Any horse that really moved its legs in some of the ways indicated by Stillman would fall flat on its face.

Muybridge published several articles and books in which the photographer showed himself to be a better scientist than the physician. The last of his books, *Animals in motion* published in London in 1899, is still the basic authority on the gaits of animals in general and of horses in particular. An illustration from this classic work is reproduced in Plate XId.

Muybridge also invented a method of printing his successive pictures on a large glass disc and projecting them in rapid succession on a screen. This device, which he called a 'zoöpraxiscope,' produced real motion pictures and it was the forerunner of our present motion-picture projector. The essential improvements made after Muybridge were the development of a camera that would take successive pictures through the same lens and the use of a celluloid strip instead of a revolving glass disc. (Photographic film was invented in 1888, after Muybridge had finished his experiments.) The modern machine is a perfected form of Edison's 'kinetoscope,' invented in 1893, and Edison derived some of his basic ideas from Muybridge. Muybridge even discussed with Edison, early in 1888, the possibility of producing talking pictures by synchronizing a zoöpraxiscope with a phonograph. The scheme was abandoned because the phonograph at that date was not loud enough to be heard by an audience. Muybridge predicted that the projection of 'visible actions simultaneously with audible words' would eventually be accomplished. We all know how right he was! Incidentally, we have not yet entirely caught up with Muybridge's predictions, because he also anticipated stereoscopic talking pictures, such that 'a perfectly realistic imitation of the original performance will be seen, in the apparent "round."' A few such motion pictures have been experimentally produced, but they are not yet fully satisfactory or in general use.

We now know the normal movements of the horse in much detail, thanks to Muybridge and to successors who have used more modern slow-motion moving-picture cameras to supplement his work (but without learning much that he did not know). One of the services rendered, and one that Muybridge himself stressed, was to show the error of most earlier representations by artists of horses in motion. The conventional drawing or painting of a running horse long showed both front legs extended straight forward beyond the low-slung head and both hind legs extended backward with hoofs turned up. (See Plate XIc) This attitude is not only unnatural but also practically impossible for a horse. Even the representations of horses walking were often incorrect. A common 'walking' pose was with one pair of diagonals (near-fore and off-hind feet, or off-fore and near-hind) both firmly planted and the other pair both flexed and in similar phases of forward motion. This is a natural attitude, but it occurs in the trot, not the walk. In the walk the four legs act in rotation and no two are in the same phase at the same time. But without further criticism of old mistakes, let us briefly take up in systematic fashion the established facts regarding the more important gaits, following Muybridge with some modifications and additions.

Horsemen recognize as many as twelve different gaits but these are all variations of four basic rhythms or cadences and systems of limb motion, seen in clearest form in the walk, trot, pace, and gallop. Variations in speed of execution and in details of successive positions account for the other more or less distinct gaits, the most important of which are summarized in Fig. 5.

The walk and the faster gaits of the same general type have a four-beat cadence, which is quite regular and without noticeable pause or interruption. The legs move forward and backward in sequence, each in its own turn. The succession of foot-falls is near-fore, off-hind, off-fore, near-hind, near-fore, etc. In the slower gaits of this kind, as seen in the normal walk, the body is alternately supported on three and on two legs. The usual support sequence is: both hind and off-fore, near-hind and off-fore, near-hind and both fore, near-hind and near-fore, both hind and near-fore, off-hind and near-fore,

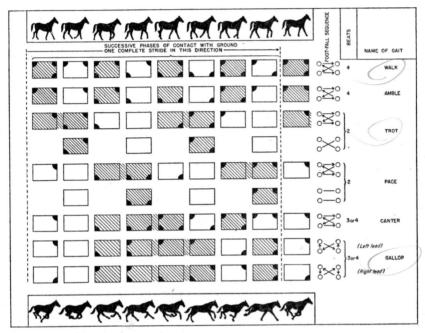

5. The gaits of the horse. Each rectangle represents a horse in a particular phase of the gait, and each horizontal line shows successive phases of the gait named to the right. In each rectangle, a black corner indicates that the corresponding foot of the horse is on the ground. Diagonal ruling indicates that a beat, or audible footfall, occurs at the beginning of this phase. Where two or three rectangles are joined by diagonal ruling, the beat is double, with two footfalls but with these normally occurring in such rapid succession that they are heard as a single beat.

off-hind and both fore, off-hind and off-fore, both hind and off-fore, and so on, repeating the eight distinct phases.

The amble, the rack, and the running walk are four-beat gaits with equal intervals between the beats as in the walk and with the same sequence of foot-falls. They differ from each other and from the walk in speed and in the extent to which they are collected or loose. The amble is practically a fast walk, with the body usually supported alternately by two feet and by one rather than by three and two as

in the walk. At the other extreme is the running walk, which still
has the walk rhythm but is freer and more rapid, a particularly loose-
jointed, swinging, uncollected gait. At top speed in this gait only
one foot is on the ground at a time and there may even be a very
brief interval between beats when no foot is on the ground. The rack
is a similar but more collected gait. The broken amble and single-
foot are variants of the rack. (Although the gaits themselves are quite
different there has been some confusion of terminology between the
amble and rack and the pace, which is also sometimes called an
amble or rack; the meanings given here are now usual in America.)
These gaits usually have to be taught, as most horses tend to break
into a trot as they increase speed above a walk.

The trot and the pace are both two-beat gaits, but the leg movement is quite different in the two. In the trot, diagonal legs move
together so that the sequence of footfalls is near-fore and off-hind,
near-hind and off-fore, near-fore and off-hind, and so on continuously.
Between beats there is an interval when all four feet are off the
ground for an instant, which occurs twice in each stride. Horses
seldom bring the two diagonal feet to the ground at precisely the
same moment and the forefoot commonly hits slightly before its
diagonal hindfoot, but the difference is usually almost imperceptible.
This makes the footfall sequence the same as in the walk. A fox-
trot, which may be counted as a separate gait in a five-gaited horse,
is simply a slow trot with slightly broken rhythm, intermediate
in speed and action between a walk and a fast trot.

The pace has the same rhythm as the trot but here it is the two
legs of the same side, not the diagonals, that move together. Here,
too, the motion is seldom absolutely simultaneous and the hindfoot
may hit imperceptibly earlier than the fore, giving again the same
footfall sequence as in the walk. The stepping pace is to the pace
what the fox-trot is to the trot, a slow, broken pace tending toward
a walk. Some horses pace naturally and a tendency either to pace
or to trot is hereditary. In most breeds, the trot is natural but
pacing can be taught. Pacing is natural in some families of harness
racers.

The gallop is the natural top-speed run of horses. It has a three-beat cadence with broken rhythm which goes as follows: beat, pause, beat, quick double-beat, beat, pause, et cetera. The corresponding sequence of footfalls (for the left lead) is: near-fore, off-hind, near-hind and off-fore almost together but the hindfoot slightly earlier, near-fore, et cetera. The 'pause' in the cadence represents a short time when all four feet are off the ground, which occurs only once in each stride as opposed to twice in the trot or pace. The off-hind foot is lifted almost immediately as the near-hind foot comes down, and before the off-fore foot hits, so that there is not normally any time when three feet are on the ground. In an extended gallop, near-hind and off-fore (on the left lead) may fall with perceptible interval and there may be four beats, but the break after the placing of the lead foot still distinguishes the cadence. The gallop differs from the gaits previously described in not being symmetrical on the two sides so that the gait may be led either on one side or the other. For the right lead, the sequence corresponding to that given above for the left lead would be: off-fore, near-hind, off-hind and near-fore, off-fore, et cetera, with the pause or leap following the off-fore. Horses can be taught to take either lead or to change from one to the other while running, an important point if the animal is to turn rapidly and safely in either direction. The horse that attempts to make a sharp running left turn on the right lead is liable to fall.

The canter, which must usually be taught if it is to be well executed, is essentially a slow, collected gallop. It has the same broken cadence as the gallop and is also performed on either right or left lead. There tend to be three beats, but a slow canter may have four beats and a pause. In distinction from the faster gallop, there are brief phases when three feet are on the ground and in a very slow canter all four feet may be on the ground at once, although this is unusual. Muybridge showed that in the canter the forefoot may hit slightly before the hind in the diagonal, double, middle beat, which gives the same footfall sequence as in the walk (but with quite different rhythm). The normal gallop sequences, given above, are different from the walk or other slower gaits.

The great majority of horses naturally have three distinct gaits, walk, trot, and gallop, with considerable variation in the speed and style of execution of each. In shows, three-gaited horses are required to walk, trot, and canter. Five-gaited horses (usually American Saddle Horses specially trained for the ring) must exhibit the walk, trot, canter, rack, and a slow gait, which may be the stepping pace, slow pace, amble, fox-trot, or running walk.

It must not be supposed that horses, even if well trained in gaits, always execute each gait with the mathematical precision of a diagram or break instantaneously from one clear-cut gait to another. Individual differences occur and the same horse, unless rigidly held in a gait at a practiced and constant speed, will introduce all sorts of minor variations as he turns, changes gaits, or varies speed within a gait.

Western horsemen sometimes insist that their horses have a fast gait which is different from any recognized in the ring and which they call a lope. As far as reliable analysis has been made, the so-called lope seems usually to be merely a smooth gallop or canter, sometimes tending to be less broken than a typical canter and verging on a four-beat rhythm similar to a running walk.

8

AMERICAN BREEDS AND THEIR FORERUNNERS

IN January, A.D. 1519, there were no horses on the American continent. Horse ancestors had lived here for 60 million years, a story to be told on later pages, but they had all died out. Their wild descendants and the domesticated horses lived on only in the Old World. In February 1519, Hernán Cortés sailed from Havana for the conquest of Mexico, and his troops took with them sixteen horses, the first to set foot on this continent since the last Ice Age horse died out some tens of thousands of years ago. Actually, seventeen horses arrived on the Mexican shore, for one of the mares foaled during the journey.

Bernal Diaz del Castillo, one of Cortés' hard-bitten companions, has left us a loving record of this historic group of animals. There were eleven stallions: four dark bay or brown, two bay, two light bay, one chestnut, and two pinto (of the type called *overo*). Three of the five mares were gray, one chestnut, and one bay. (These are not the colors given in English translations of this passage from Diaz del Castillo. I am following Dr. A. Cabrera, a great authority on the Spanish language and on horses, who has shown that the translators into English have all been mistaken, especially in thinking that the color called *castaño* in Spanish was chestnut; it was the color we call bay.)

These horses and the other Spanish horses that came after them made and changed history. The conquest would have been impossible without them. Their introduction later permitted the Indians to strike back and, among the plains tribes, to develop a character-

istic and picturesque but transitory horse culture. They made possible, too, the development of the cattle range and the ranch life
that has left an indelible stamp on the character of the West and of
Westerners.

There is a tale, so often repeated that it has become almost a part
of the American credo, that the early mustang bands and, from
them, the old cowpony and Indian pony were derived from a few
horses that escaped from the parties led by De Soto and by Coronado.
Francis Haines and other recent students have established beyond
doubt that there is no truth in this legend. The acquisition of horses
by the Indians and the origin of the wild herds were by less romantic
and more effective means.

The early Indian horses of the Southwest were acquired, for the
most part, from missions and from traders. The Spanish missions
were often cattle ranches as well, and secular cattle ranches followed
close behind them in some areas. The cattle were, of course, worked
on horseback and Indians were often employed as *vaqueros*. So they
learned to ride and to know the value of the horse, and not infre-
quently they fled from the ranches with stolen mounts. Sometimes
they would return in the night with fellow tribesmen to steal more
horses. As the demand grew, traders, often half-breeds, drove horses
into Indian country and bartered them among the tribes. Many of
the Indians were already mounted before feral horses were common in their territories. The feral herds—the 'wild horses' of western
history—arose from horses that escaped from the missions, ranches,
and Indians, and not from those ridden by the explorers. Sensibly,
the Indian much preferred stealing or trading for domesticated
animals to capturing and breaking the recalcitrant mustangs, although these came to be an additional source of supply.

Throughout most of what is now the United States and all of
Latin America, the earliest domestic horses were Spanish. On the
Atlantic coast, horses of Spanish descent spread north from Florida.
Even as far as New England, where the early horses were mostly of
English origin, some Spanish blood came to be intermingled and to
have its influence. Throughout the West, the early horses were
almost pure Spanish. Their blood has since been mingled with that

of many other strains, but most of the characteristic American breeds and types of today probably have some remote or near Spanish influence.

There has been much discussion about the breeds and types of these Spanish horses and much that has been said about them is pure fantasy. The most reliable authority on this subject is undoubtedly Ángel Cabrera, an eminent zoologist who has studied these horses and their history with extreme care, both in Spain and in Argentina, where the old type is probably more nearly preserved than anywhere else. He says, 'American races of horses developed in regions discovered and colonized by the Spanish are descendants of the old Andalusian horse, which had more Barb than anything else in its make-up, although with modifications resulting from four and a half centuries of acclimatization [in Spain].' These Andalusian horses were jennets or jinetas, descended in part from older, even prehistoric, Spanish races but with a predominant Barb element brought in by the Arab conquerors from North Africa. The invading 'Arabs' were, in fact, Arabized Berbers and not Arabians from Arabia. Their horses doubtless had some touch of Arabian blood, but this was relatively slight and there is no evidence that a purebred Arabian horse ever reached Spain before modern times.

The conformation of the Andalusian horse that gave American horses their Spanish blood has also been reconstructed by Cabrera from old paintings and records. 'It was an animal rather small than large, quite medium (mesomorph) in type, generally rather close to the ground, with an ample barrel, wide chest, muscular and rather short neck, rounded and sloping croup, and tail set quite low—these last two being typical points of the Barb.' They displayed the whole range of horse colors, including the various sorts of spotting, although spotting was not especially characteristic.

The word 'mustang' is a monument to the inability of the early English-speaking westerners to pronounce the Spanish word *mesteño*. The mustangs or mesteños were originally the feral horses, the 'wild herds,' the horses that belonged to nobody, and in their original form they were probably almost pure Spanish. Some of these were caught and broken and 'mustang' came to mean also a cowpony of what had become the native western stock, with little or no infusion of more cultured strains. The years of fending for themselves in the wilds had changed the offspring of the proud Andalusian type, and the mustang lacked much in size, grace, and finish. It was, however, a horse of almost incredible stamina and endurance and was also exceptionally alert and intelligent.

There is much mustang blood in western horses today, but the old type of cowpony has been extensively crossed with other breeds to increase its speed, size, and general appearance. A historic horse and one with highly admirable traits of its own has thus been all but lost to us. There are breeders and associations for exploiting all sorts of color combinations and other novel, attractive, but not particularly vital characteristics, but there is no organized effort to save or to restore the mustang as a valuable part of our heritage. It is probably not too late, even now, but the time is getting short. What could be done has been demonstrated in some South American countries, particularly in the Argentine. There a breeding stock of the old sturdy ponies was gathered from remote parts of the country, especially far back in the Patagonian wilderness, and the type has been preserved in an admirable, increasingly valued registered breed, the Criollo.

The Indian ponies contained much of the mustang and a little of every other kind of horse that the Indians could lay hands on. The cayuse, as Indian ponies in general came to be called after one tribe of horse Indians, varied, and still varies, enormously in type, but has typically been a runty and unkempt animal that does not represent the true qualities of the mustang. Some Indian ponies are of mustang type, but in general they are inferior to the old, true mustang and the confusion of cayuse and mustang is unfortunate for the latter. That cayuses became degenerate animals was an inevitable result of the Indians' complete carelessness in breeding and of their riding the best stallions while the worst stallions ran with the mares.

While the mustangs were spreading in the West, and similar types through the south even to the Atlantic coast, settlers in the more thickly populated eastern English colonies were importing many fine horses from the Old World. In the different conditions of the New World and with the different needs and tastes of breeders here, selection was made for various distinctive types. With later refinements and modifications by crossing and out-crossing, these eventually became the several outstanding purely American breeds now registered in this country: the Standard Bred trotters and pacers, the Morgans, the Quarter Horses, the American Saddle Horses, and the Tennessee Walking Horses.

Smart, fast carriage horses were highly prized by our ancestors and a natural outcome of their pride in such horses was harness racing. The intense interest in this sport was fostered in this country, beyond most others, by puritanical objections to running races. Apparently impromptu brushes between rival 'roadsters' were not really races, and consciences, as well as the law, were appeased by the theory that a trotting horse is not traveling at top speed and therefore is not racing in the sinful sense of the word! In any case, trotting races achieved greater popularity here than in other countries, and they continue on a large scale and on a well-organized basis even now that carriage horses are rarities outside the track and the show ring.

Good trotting horses were of diverse origins and were long bred without any one fixed standard. A register was established in 1871 on the basis of racing performance of the animals and their progeny. With increasing emphasis on blood lines rather than performance alone, a highly standardized type was produced under the name of Standard Bred. The modern Standard Bred horses are largely of Thoroughbred origin and derive from Messenger, a Thoroughbred running horse imported from England in 1788. Among several families, the Hambletonian has become dominant, originating in Rysdyk's Hambletonian, a descendant of Messenger in three lines, foaled in 1849. Greyhound, the horse that established a harness trotting record of a mile in 1:55¼ in 1938, came from four generations of sires and three of dams all directly descended from Rysdyk's Hambletonian. The Standard Bred registry also includes pacers, now almost identical in blood with the trotters and achieving about the same speed—the record for a paced mile is 1:55.

The Standard Bred horse (Plate XIIa) closely resembles the Thoroughbred, but averages somewhat smaller, about 15:2 hands, and tends to be somewhat longer, lower, and sturdier. Harness races are still run in heats, requiring each horse to trot or race the distance three times (usually) for each race and calling for greater stamina than is demanded from a Thoroughbred runner.

The Morgan (Plate XIIb) is unique among breeds in owing its existence to a single great progenitor, a small bay stallion named (after its owner) Justin Morgan. This is the only breed named after a horse. (The Hambletonians are a family whose breed is the Standard Bred.) Justin Morgan was of unknown ancestry and there have been endless speculations and arguments as to the source of the qualities of this remarkable sire which lived in Vermont from 1795, a few years after being foaled, until his death in 1821. There is good evidence that Justin Morgan had Thoroughbred blood, but he must also have had considerable 'cold' blood and was quite distinct from the Thoroughbred in conformation. This conformation and the accompanying performance have been remarkably sustained in the descendants of the Morgan breed. Registry was established in 1893 and is now closed (that is, registered sire and dam are required for registry). Nearly 700 Morgans were registered in 1947.

Justin Morgan was a mere pony standing about 14 hands, but modern Morgans tend to be somewhat larger, ranging usually from 14:2 to 15:2 hands and 1000 to 1200 pounds. They are broad, muscular, short-legged horses, sturdier and less slender than most of the show types of saddle horses. The head is broad, with large eyes, heavy jaw, and fine muzzle.

The early Morgans were harness racers but they had to give way on the tracks to other less sturdy, yet faster trotting families, especially the Hambletonians. Outside of racing, they preserved their esteem as roadsters and general useful light horses, usually in harness. The passing of the carriage threatened their existence and led to something of a crisis in their breeding, but the problem has been met by developing them into excellent saddle horses. They are still bred in Vermont and elsewhere in the northeast but breeding is even more active in the west, especially in California. There is some difference of aim between the two areas, as the eastern breeders often prefer a larger horse, nearer the Saddler type, upward of 15 hands, while western taste runs to a smaller type (to that extent, at least, more like the prototype Justin Morgan), useful as a stock horse as well as a general pleasure horse. Morgans are also much valued for cross-breeding to produce utility grades.

A type distinctively American, only lately established and recognized as a breed, but with a long history on this continent, is represented by the Quarter Horses. (Plate XIIc) They first appeared in the southern English colonies, especially in Virginia, and carried much Spanish blood from the old Spanish territories to southward and from the southeastern equivalents of the western mustangs. In time this stock was extensively crossed with imported English horses, especially Thoroughbreds, the most famous of which was Janus, which landed in Virginia in 1752. A short, thick, stocky horse was produced with the specialty of getting off to a quick start and maintaining high speed over short distances. Neighborhood races were run on straight race paths about a quarter-mile in length and the quarter-mile racer became the Quarter Horse. Even the Thoroughbred was left at the post and beaten in these short races, although the Quarter Horse has little chance against a good Thoroughbred on the longer track.

The passing of pioneer conditions, development of course racing, and preference for the more slender and stylish Thoroughbred and related types led to the decline of the Quarter Horse in its original home. There are those who say that much Quarter Horse blood was bred into the American Thoroughbred lines before the days of closed registries. Others claim that Justin Morgan was a Quarter Horse, a point difficult to prove or dispute in view of the facts that Justin Morgan's ancestry is unrecorded and that with no register in existence any sturdy short racer of that time might well be called a Quarter Horse. However that may be, the Quarter Horse type itself was not lost but simply moved, with some modification, to a different region, the Southwest.

The modern Quarter Horse is bred and valued throughout a large region, but breeding centers particularly in Texas. A number of famous families have arisen there, among them those tracing to Steel Dust, foaled in 1843 in Illinois, and to Shilo, foaled in 1844 in Tennessee, both taken to Texas in the later 1840's. There has also been repeated infusion of Thoroughbred blood in order to eliminate a certain tendency toward coarseness in conformation and to improve performance by lengthening the run. Registry was not established until 1940 and is based on blood, conformation, and performance, or any two of these for tentative registry, with closed registry anticipated as a goal.

The modern Quarter Horse type is low, 15 hands or less, but relatively heavy for this height, up to 1200 pounds. The head is short, broad, with short ears, sometimes rather bulldoggish in aspect. Shoulders are deep and sloping, the chest broad, and the back short. The legs are tremendously muscled and are short, with particularly short, stout cannons. These horses are still used in short races and often appear in rodeos. They are, however, basically utility horses and are particularly valuable for working cattle, a task for which their agility, flash starting and quick turning, and calm co-operative temperament may make them ideal.

Among riding horses, almost the opposite extreme from the stocky Quarter Horse in general conformation is the American Saddle Horse. (Plate XIId) The type dates back with minor variations for some four hundred years and started developing in the early days of the English colonies as what the name implies descriptively: an American general purpose riding horse. Early horses of this general type were imported mainly from England. A distinctive American type developed as an amalgam not only of English riding horses but also of others from Spain, France, North Africa, and elsewhere. The desire was for a light, speedy, handsome, and tractable animal for travel in the days when rapid travel was on horseback. The Kentucky saddle horse, forerunner of the present breed, was well established as a type even before the importation of

Denmark, a four-mile racer foaled in 1839, now recognized as foundation sire of the breed. Standard Bred, Morgan, and other strains have also been introduced, but Thoroughbred blood has come to predominate. Since the establishment of the American Saddle Horse Breeders Association in 1891, 'American Saddle Horse' is the name of a definite breed and not merely the description of a type.

The present-day American Saddle Horse (often called simply the 'Saddle Horse' or 'Saddler') is one of the showiest of all animals, the acclaimed 'peacock of the horse world.' Small head, long neck, small, light barrel, flat croup, long, sloping pastern, generally light, close-knit but not chunky conformation, all combine to give the horse inimitable grace and elegance. Height runs from 15 to about 16:2 hands, although the latter extreme is rather tall for the preference of most riders. Dark colors with usually inconspicuous light markings are prevalent. The horse is highly spirited but obedient and learns to execute three or five gaits with precision and brilliant action. The three-gaited and five-gaited horses are usually of slightly different type, with the latter somewhat heavier.

The American Saddle Horse is mainly bred and trained for horse-show purposes and has come to dominate the show ring. In spite of this specialization, this remains an excellent horse for all saddle purposes and has many friends whose interest goes beyond that of competition in shows. It may also be judiciously used to produce useful grade horses and to improve the lines and action of less showy or more sluggish strains. Its popularity is attested by over 4,000 registrations in 1947.

Among the most recent of breeds and one rapidly increasing in popularity is the Tennessee Walking Horse (Plate XIIe), also widely but unofficially designated the Plantation Walker. The foundation sire was Allan, foaled in 1886 in Kentucky and taken to Tennessee as a colt. Allan was a black Standard Bred trotter from Hambletonian and Morgan strains. Thoroughbred and American Saddle Bred ancestors also contributed, but the Walking Horse is almost as much of a one-sire breed as the Morgan and might almost be called 'the Allan.' The Stud Book was established in 1935 and registration is closed.

In conformation, Walking Horses resemble the American Saddle Horse but they are usually more robust and rugged, weighing 1000 to 1200 pounds with an average height under 16 hands. They were originally all-purpose horses, strong enough for light draft and general farm work but also useful and comfortable under the saddle. They are now primarily pleasure riding horses and are lately being trained and shown extensively in special three-gaited classes, their show gaits being the walk, canter, and running walk. The running walk has given the breed its name and is a specialty of these excellent horses, although it usually requires careful training for good performance and some walkers tend to break into a pace, an uncomfortable gait in a riding horse.

A word may here be said about polo ponies, although these are not a breed and are not exclusively American. A polo pony is simply any horse trained and used for playing polo. Horses adaptable for this highly specialized use are necessarily somewhat uniform in type: small, fast, agile, and courageous. In England there is a registry for polo ponies, but these are usually not purebred. Many of them represent crosses between a large, fast breed and one of the breeds of ponies, for instance between Thoroughbred and Welsh pony. Argentine polo ponies have sometimes been Criollos (the native breed similar to our old mustangs) but are now usually crosses of Thoroughbred on Criollo. In the United States a corresponding type of polo pony is obtained by breeding Thoroughbred stallions on Western cowpony mares. Purebred and grade Quarter Horses may also be trained for polo, and Morgan and Arabian blood may likewise be desirable for this purpose. The important thing in a polo pony is not so much its blood lines as its aptitude for the game, and it is painstaking training that makes a polo pony and gives it value.

9

A HORSE OF ANOTHER COLOR

MOHAMMED is reputed to have said, 'If thou hast a dark chestnut horse, ride him into combat.' Other Arab sayings would have it that white horses are princely but do not stand heat, that bay horses are sturdiest, that all horses but bays are unlucky unless they have some white markings, that chestnuts are exceptionally fast but hot tempered—and so on. Many a western rancher insists that dun horses are hardiest and have the best cow sense. The Phantom Mustang of western folklore, with its super-equine speed and super-human wits, was always represented as milk-white.

Others say that any color is good on a good horse.

For all their color prejudices and superstitions, the Arabs do breed horses of almost every color. Few breeds are purer or reproduce more strictly to type than do Arabians, and yet there is no standard or 'right' color for them. Our highly inbred and rigidly typed Thoroughbreds may be black, brown, bay, chestnut, dun, gray, strawberry roan, blue roan, or various shades of these, as listed in the color guide of the Jockey Club. Duns are far from monopolizing the spectrum of western range horses, nor are milk-white mustangs in general favor.

The fact is that color, conformation, and performance do not necessarily go together and that to this extent it is true that any color is good on a good horse. It would undoubtedly be possible, by controlled and well-planned breeding, to produce any possible type of horse with all the colors natural to horses. Some breeds are characterized by a predominant or exclusive color: most Percherons are gray (but some are black) and all Suffolks are chestnut. This

is only an accidental result of breeding in a limited stock or a re-
flection of color preferences among early breeders. The color may
be changed when preferences change: the Flemish horse was black
but its modern descendant, the Belgian, is usually sorrel or chestnut
(occasionally bay, gray, or black). There is no reason to think that
a pinto Percheron or a palomino Suffolk would be inferior—or
superior—to those of the usual colors.

Yet it would not be true to say that the color of a horse makes no
difference at all. For one thing, when some color has been fixed in a
breed, or eliminated from the breed, its absence or presence betrays
outcrossing. It would be a fairly safe conclusion that any Suffolk
that is not chestnut is not purebred, whether as a horse it is the
better or the worse for whatever crossing has occurred. Spotting has
been rigidly excluded from the heredity of almost all the recognized
pure breeds, so that it is a safe bet that a spotted horse, however fine
in type, is not a purebred Thoroughbred, Saddle Horse, Standard
Bred, Morgan, et cetera. It might actually be a better horse than
some purebred horses of these and related breeds, but it would not
be purebred. Thus color is to some extent associated with breed
and so may be an indication of what you have in a horse, but it is
only part of the label not of the contents of the package.

There is an idea that light-colored horses do better in some cli-
mates and dark horses in others, but this is only a possibility. The
difference, if it exists, is not obvious and probably not of much practical significance. The eyes and skins of the palest horses may be sensitive to burning sunlight, but if so, this does not particularly matter
if the horses are not worked for long periods in the sun. There is
little evidence that any horse color is good or bad in itself and simply
as a color.

Color is important, but its chief importance is in the eye of the
beholder. Anyone who uses horses or who likes them for any reason
likes to look at them. Appearance is a major part of their appeal, and
nothing makes more difference in appearance than does color. But
then the best color is simply a matter of taste, and tastes differ.
This is fortunate. How monotonous it would be if all horses had

the same color! And they would soon all have the same color if all horse breeders and users preferred one color and this bred true.

There is no fully satisfactory classification of horse colors and no really sharp distinction between colors and patterns, but the names are fairly well standardized. The most important of these are:

BLACK. This means true black as ground color throughout, although white blaze and stockings may occur. Black usually breeds true, but black to black matings occasionally produce a bay foal, suggesting that there may be two kinds of black horses as regards their heredity.

BROWN. In horses, 'brown' does not cover the same range as in common speech. It applies to horses that are black or nearly so, except for lighter areas around the muzzle and eyes and on the legs. In breeding, brown is a rather tricky and unpredictable color. It is not always correctly distinguished from black, and true brown usually acts in breeding as if it were dark bay or dark chestnut.

BAY. Bay horses have black mane, tail, and (usually) stockings. The main coat color presents shades of brown, red brown, or tan, varying from dark (mahogany bay), sometimes difficult to tell from brown as defined above, through medium red shades (blood bay) to pale (sandy bay). Bay is generally considered a basic color, but in a sense it is a pattern, since it may differ from shades of chestnut only in the presence of the black points. Bay can be fixed so that it breeds true, but some bays have mixed color heredity and can produce chestnuts or other colors.

CHESTNUT. Chestnut horses are shades of flat brown, red brown, or golden, without the black points of bay. Dark shades are liver chestnut. Lighter red or golden shades are usually called sorrel. Chestnuts usually breed true, that is, mating chestnut to chestnut almost always produces a chestnut foal.

PALOMINO. Palominos have flaxen or silvery manes and tails combined with golden coats, varying from rich reddish or bronze to pale yellow or dark cream, resembling the lighter shades of chestnut or sorrel, ranging into diluted sorrel. An old Spanish name for these color combinations is ysabella or isabel. Palominos at present do not breed true for color, introducing a problem that will be discussed farther along in this chapter.

DUN. Strictly speaking, dun is a dull grayish or yellowish color, but the name may be applied to a diluted or smoky effect on any of the basic colors. Usage differs somewhat, but dun in horses usually also implies the presence of a black stripe down the back, often with other black points or stripes across withers or on the legs, on a washed-out base color. Many descriptive names are somewhat unsystematically applied to variations: mouse dun, coyote dun, buckskin dun, et cetera. From the breeding point of view, more than one type of color is involved in dun. Most duns do not breed true.

CREAM. Very pale diluted sorrel or yellow color may best be called cream or cremello, although some consider it an extremely pale palomino or ysabella and others classify it as the extreme of dun. The color may be nearly white and called pseudo-albino or albino ('Albino A,' see 'white,' below), although it is not true albino. The color usually breeds true.

WHITE. Very pale color or absence of any pigment in the hairs of the coat is designated white, but in reality there are several quite distinct sorts of white in horses and the different whites do not behave in the same way in color heredity in breeding. Many whites are simply old grays, in which the white hairs increasing with age (as they do in most men) have practically replaced the black hairs with which these horses are born. Horses that are born very pale or white are called albinos by most breeders and may now even be officially registered as such. In the strictest technical sense, there are probably no true albino horses. An albino in this technical usage is an animal that is by heredity unable to produce any pigment whatever in hair, skin, or eyes and that cannot pass on to its offspring the ability to produce pigment. As far as known, all 'albino' horses have some pigment or have a factor for pigment that can be passed on to offspring. Three distinct sorts of 'albino' or pseudo-albino horses, called 'Albino A, B, or W,' have been definitely identified and others are possible. 'Albino A' has the body ivory, mane pure white, eyes blue ('glass'), and skin pink. 'Albino B,' apparently very rare, has the mane buff, slightly darker than the body. 'Albino W' has pure white hair and pink skin, but usually has brown eyes. 'A' and 'B' breed true, and 'W' tends to do so but does occasionally produce colored foals. Extreme roaning or extreme white spotting (see below) may also produce horses that are mainly or nearly white. White stockings, blaze, or spots are not, as many horsemen have thought, 'the beginnings of albinism.' They are separate hereditary characters entirely distinct from white color of the coat as a whole.

GRAY. Grays are usually born dark brown or black. White hairs begin to appear as the animals become older and they may eventually become almost pure white. Some grays breed true and others have mixed color heredity. In the latter case, gray to gray matings produce about three-fourths gray foals and about one-fourth other colors.

ROAN. Roan is not a base color but an effect produced by a rather uniform sprinkling of white hairs mixed with other colors. Blue roans are roaned blacks, usually with some red or yellow hairs in addition to black and white. Red roan is roaned bay, and strawberry roan is roaned chestnut or sorrel. In breeding, roan acts like gray; some breed true and some produce about one-fourth unroaned foals.

PINTO. Pinto is becoming the preferred name for a variety of spotted patterns of white and any other color, which have also been given a number of other names: paint, calico, pied, piebald, skewbald, particolored, et cetera. Piebald strictly means spotted white and black and skewbald white and any color but black. The Pinto Horse Society rejects these names and distinguishes overo and tobiano, names borrowed from the Argentine. On overos, the white spreads irregularly upward from the belly, the base color is frequently roaned, back, mane, and tail are usually dark, the legs are seldom all white, and the face is commonly bald. On tobianos, the white spreads down from the back, its borders are usually clean-cut, mane and tail may be white spotted or white, white stockings are usual, and the head is colored but may have a blaze. In heredity, there seem to be several types of pintos but these are not very well worked out at present. Some breed true but others may not.

APPALOOSA. This is also a spotted pattern, sometimes included under pinto but apparently distinct. The usual character is a white patch over hips and loin with scattered dark spots. The skin itself is particolored and the hoofs are striped. Other details are extremely variable.

Every one of these colors, wth all of their varieties, has its fanciers. Dun is perhaps the least flashy and it has been considered the most plebian of colors, yet duns occur in many pure breeds, including the Thoroughbred. The preference of some western ranchers for duns has been mentioned, and it may have a solid basis in the mere fact that duns are not much in demand for breeding fancy pleasure or show horses. Western strains running to duns may thus have been crossed less and may have remained nearer to the old, cow-wise, mustang type of horse. Some of these duns might help to establish a good foundation stock for bringing back the mustang type or forming a North American *criollo* breed. Such an attempt cannot, however, be a success if breeding is primarily for color rather than type. Moreover, the mustang type certainly included a great variety of colors, as does the present South American criollo breed, and in fact dun often does not breed true.

To an increasing number of horse devotees palomino-colored horses are 'the most beautiful in the world.' Anyone who has seen a palomino of fine breed or type will find it hard to disagree with this sentiment. (See Plate XIIIa) All good horses are beautiful, but their admirers put golden horses with silver manes and tails in a class by themselves. Recently some of these admirers have literally put them in a class apart, taking the unusual step of establishing a registry for horses of this color.

There are, indeed, two national associations promoting palomino horses and registering them. There are also two schools of philosophy or faith in regard to the aims and probable outcome of this movement. The older organization, established in 1932 with headquarters in California, is the Palomino Horse Association. This group has gone on record as proposing to establish a breed of horses which is to be invariably palomino in color and of fine riding type, with mares standing about 15 hands, stallions averaging 15:3, and around 1100 pounds in weight. Present registration requirements are rigid regarding color but make no very strict demands about blood or type beyond specifying that the adult size be above that of a pony (14:2 or over).

The other palomino association, the Palomino Horse Breeders of America, founded in 1941 and with national headquarters in Texas, recognizes that palomino is a color, not a breed or a type. There seems to be some difference of opinion among the members whether the association should aim at ultimate establishment of a separate breed of palomino-colored horses or whether this is feasible. In the meantime the immediate and practical aim is to promote the breeding of palomino horses in the established breeds and in desirable types of conformation and performance.

The dispute about color, breed, and type, and about the aims of palomino breeding arises from the fact that at present palomino color does not breed true. A foal with both sire and dam palominos is not always palomino itself, and it is doubtful whether this color can ever be fixed in breeding lines. The issue involves fundamental processes of color inheritance in horses. The full details of these processes are quite complicated and a complete discussion of color heredity is outside the scope of this book. The essentials are, however, fairly simple and have much interest not only because of the palomino problem but also because they are a good example of how heredity works in general, and not only in determining the colors of foals.

When two animals (or two humans, for that matter) mate and produce offspring, each parent passes on one set of determiners of heredity (genes) to that offspring. In horses, then, the foal receives one set of color determiners from its sire and one set from its dam. The parents each have two sets and pass on one; the foal also has two, one from each parent. In each set there are several different kinds of determiners. One, commonly called A, is a pattern determiner. When this is present along with a determiner for black, labeled B, it makes the black color appear in the mane and tail (generally also on the lower legs). An animal that has both an A and a B is a bay (unless there are some other determiners in the set that modify this). If the animal has an A and a B in one set and also an A and a B in another set, its total of these determiners is $AB + AB$, or $AABB$ for short. Both sets are alike (the students of heredity call them 'homo-zygous'). If two animals of this sort mate, then each must pass on one *A* and one *B* to the foal, so the foal also must have *AB* (from the sire) + *AB* (from the dam) or *AABB*. This sire and dam are both the same color, bay, and all their offspring will always be bay; they breed true for color. (See Fig. 6)

There is, however, another form of *A*, which is labeled *a* and which means that the pattern determiner does not work. Another form of *B*, labeled *b*, produces pure brown color without any black. If an animal has the double set *AaBb*, it will still be a bay, because only one *A* and one *B* are necessary to make bay. (In technical terms, *A* and *B* are dominant; the effects of either of these appear even if only one *A* or *B* is present. The alternative forms *a* and *b* are reces-sive; their effects appear only if there are two *a*'s or two *b*'s present.) But if two animals of this type are mated, their foals will not all be bay. A foal can receive either *A* or *a* and either *B* or *b* from its sire and either also in each case from the dam. Therefore these different sorts of double sets are possible in the foals:

AABB
AaBB — Foals with these sets will all be bay, like the parents, because
AABb — these double sets all contain both *A* and *B*.
AaBb

AAbb — Foals with these double sets have no determiner for black, *B*.
Aabb — They will be all brown (of one shade or another) and will be
aabb — chestnuts or sorrels in horse color terms, in spite of the fact that both parents were bays.

aaBB — Both of these produce black foals, because they have the black
aaBb — determiner, *B*, but do not have the pattern determiner, *A*, that would confine the black to mane, tail, and legs.

Bays with the formula *AaBb* thus will not breed true, but as a broad average for every nine bay foals that they produce there will be four chestnuts and three blacks. (See Fig. 7) If animals are to breed true for bay, they must have the formula *AABB*. By careful breeding it is possible to produce a stock of animals of this type and it will then breed true for color as long as there is no out-crossing. This has been done in the case of the Cleveland Bays. The same thing can be done for most other colors. Chestnuts always breed true (unless some modifying factor not *A, a, B,* or *b* is involved) because they all have the combination *bb* and their offspring must also all be *bb* and therefore chestnuts. Grays, roans, and some others are like bays in that they can be made to breed true but do not necessarily do so.

Now there is another determiner which comes in two forms, *D* and *d. D* tends to dilute or make paler the basic color; *d* does not. A double dose of *D,* formula *DD,* is necessary to produce extreme paleness and a *D* from only one parent, making the foal's formula *Dd,* produces only partial dilution. The evidence strongly suggests that palominos have the pattern determiners, either *AA* or *Aa,* the chestnut determiners, *bb,* and also the *partial* dilution determiners, *Dd.* This part of their color heredity formula is thus probably *AAbbDd* or *AabbDd.* The formulas *AAbbDD* and *AabbDD,* with full dilution, produce pale cream or the so-called albino type A. The formulas *AAbbdd* and *Aabbdd* produce chestnuts.

When two palominos of, say, formula *AAbbDd* are mated, half their foals, on an average, will also have *AAbbDd* and will be palominos. But a quarter, as a broad average over a large number of such matings, will inherit two *D*'s, and they will be cream or 'Albino A' in color, and another quarter will inherit two *d*'s and they will be chestnut. The situation, according to this theory, is that a palomino has to inherit *different* determiners from sire and dam. (See Fig. 8) If this is correct, then it is absolutely impossible for palomino color to breed true. Palomino to palomino breeding will always produce some chestnut and some cream or pseudo-albino foals. The only way to be sure to get a palomino foal is to mate horses of two other colors, 'Albino A' and chestnut.

No one supposes that we now know absolutely everything about color inheritance in horses and it is remotely possible that palomino color can be determined in some other way. At present, however, the chances of fixing this color in a breed seem very slim indeed. The only way to learn more is to keep careful records of all foals in palomino breeding, regardless of their color. Palomino registration is useless for this, because it omits mention of foals of other colors. Attempts are now being made to secure the necessary records, and

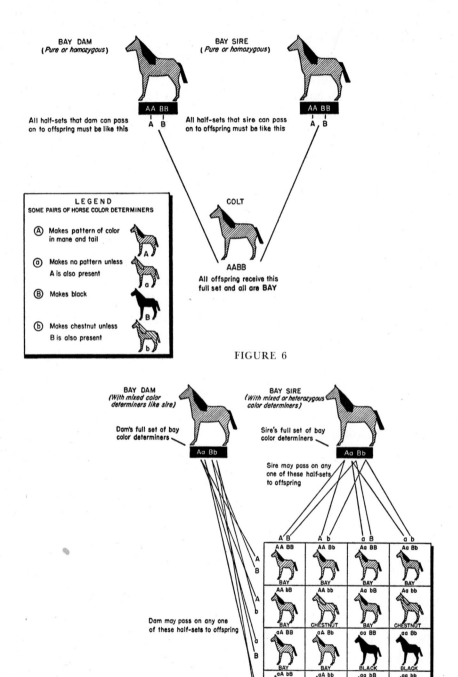

BAY DAM
(Pure or homozygous)

All half-sets that dam can pass
on to offspring must be like this

AA BB
A B

BAY SIRE
(Pure or homozygous)

All half-sets that sire can pass
on to offspring must be like this

AA BB
A B

COLT

AABB

All offspring receive this
full set and all are BAY

LEGEND
SOME PAIRS OF HORSE COLOR DETERMINERS

(A) Makes pattern of color
in mane and tail

(a) Makes no pattern unless
A is also present

(B) Makes black

(b) Makes chestnut unless
B is also present

FIGURE 6

BAY DAM
*(With mixed color
determiners like sire)*

Dam's full set of bay
color determiners

Aa Bb

BAY SIRE
*(With mixed or heterozygous
color determiners)*

Sire's full set of bay
color determiners

Aa Bb

Sire may pass on any
one of these half-sets
to offspring

Dam may pass on any one
of these half-sets to offspring

A B	A b	a B	a b
AA BB BAY	AA Bb BAY	Aa BB BAY	Aa Bb BAY
AA bB BAY	AA bb CHESTNUT	Aa bB BAY	Aa bb CHESTNUT
aA BB BAY	aA Bb BAY	aa BB BLACK	aa Bb BLACK
aA bB BAY	aA bb CHESTNUT	aa bB BLACK	aa bb CHESTNUT

FIGURE 7

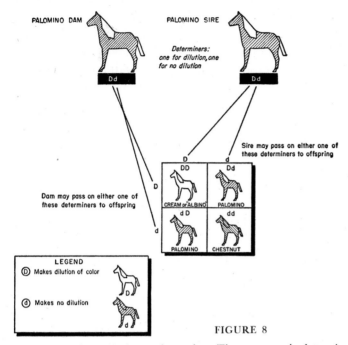

PALOMINO DAM   PALOMINO SIRE

Determiners:
one for dilution, one
for no dilution

Dd   Dd

Sire may pass on either one of
these determiners to offspring

Dam may pass on either one of
these determiners to offspring

D   d
D
DD   Dd

CREAM or ALBINO   PALOMINO
d D   dd
d
PALOMINO   CHESTNUT

LEGEND
Ⓓ Makes dilution of color

Ⓓ D

Ⓓ Makes no dilution

Ⓓ d

FIGURE 8

6. Color inheritance in horses, bay x bay. The way genetic determiners combine from parents to offspring to fix the color of the foal. This case is the relatively simple one of dam and sire both pure (homozygous) for bay color, always producing bay foals. (See text for further explanation.)

7. Color inheritance in horses, bay x bay, with both dam and sire mixed (heterozygous) in their genetic determiners. The checkerboard diagram shows all possibly resulting colors of foals in the proportions in which they would occur on an average as a result of many such matings. (Symbols as in Fig. 7; see text for further explanation.)

8. Color inheritance, palomino x palomino. The most probable current theory of palomino color inheritance, showing that on an average among many palomino x palomino matings only half the offspring will be palominos. Determiners for chestnut color and for pattern are also present. (See Fig. 6) (For further explanation, see text.)

these should eventually settle the question. (For a more complete, but somewhat more technical, account of color inheritance in horses, read the article by the leading authority, W. E. Castle, cited at the end of this book.)

In the meantime the palomino breeders are not wasting their time. At worst, they can produce strains or families in which, as an average over the years, half the foals are palominos and the others are also horses of desirable breed or type although not of palomino color. The Palomino Horse Breeders of America are doing an especially worth-while job by emphasizing breeding by type. They distinguish type or breed classes in the palomino registry and promote purebred or high-class grade Arabians, Quarter Horses, Saddle Horses, Thoroughbreds, Morgans, Tennessee Walking Horses, and Standard Bred horses that are of the prized color. Many of these horses are purebred and have double registry, in their breed and in the palomino color register. This is particularly true of Tennessee Walking Horses, Morgans, and Quarter Horses. The palomino color is rare or absent among purebred Arabians and Thoroughbreds, but grades, from half-bred up to $^{31}\!/_{32}$ of purebred ancestry, may be palominos.

Most breeders have scorned pintos. Spotting has often been taken as indicative in itself of mixed ancestry or undesirable hybridization. This is wholly false. Calico spotting or pinto pattern is usually due to another color determinant which is inherited in the same way as black or bay and which could be bred into, or out of any strain or type of horses. The pattern is not really a mixture of colors and does not result from crossing white and colored horses. With a few exceptions, pinto foals have at least one pinto parent. As far as known, pinto has never characterized any one definite breed or type and does not indicate any particular origin or mixture of blood. Most pure-breed registries exclude pintos from registration, and this has eliminated the pinto hereditary determinants from these breeds. This has the result that the pinto pattern does indicate that the horse cannot be a purebred Saddle Horse for instance. In combination with selection for type, pinto coloration could nevertheless be developed in a breed as good as any other. This is the aim of the Pinto Horse Society, an association of enthusiasts who far from scorning the parti-colored horses place a high value on their gay and flashy patterns—a matter of taste again, and wise men long ago warned against disputing about tastes.

The society recognizes overo and tobiano (see above) and in the latest stud books also appaloosa (see below) as variations of the accepted pinto patterns. They have now set standards for two types. The proposed conformation of the Western Saddle Horse Pinto resembles that of the modern Quarter Horse, while the American Parade Pinto is similar to an American Saddle Horse. (See Plate XIIIb)

The peculiar and less widely known appaloosa spotting (Plate XIIIc) is also the object of a separate association, the Appaloosa Horse Club. The origin of the name is disputed, but it is probably derived from the Palouse River, in the far Northwest. The Nez Percé Indians formerly ranged that country and many of their horses had the peculiar spotting now called appaloosa. In Oregon, a strain of these western range horses has been crossed with Arabian, and the club is developing a good type of spotted riding horse, ranging 14:2 to 16 hands and 900 to 1100 pounds. At present appaloosa, like pinto, must be considered merely a color pattern and not a breed, but there is no apparent reason why a real breed cannot be developed from this stock.

Similar horses with highly variable appaloosa patterns are bred in Colorado under the name of Colorado Rangers. They are derived in large part from relatively recent Andalusian, Barb, and Arabian importations, and their developers insist on the absence of any Appaloosa blood, as far as this applies to descendants of the Indian ponies. But (as R. M. Denhardt, the Quarter Horse specialist and western horse authority, has also pointed out) the Oregon appaloosas also boast Andalusian, Barb, and Arabian descent, and the difference does not seem too important.

White horses, popularly but not quite correctly called 'albinos,' also have their special champions. They are promoted especially by the Thompsons of White Horse Ranch in Nebraska, who have organized an American Albino Horse Club. The club has a registry for horses of this color, which is in fact an absence or extreme dilution of color. Eligible horses must be born white and must have pink skins. The great majority of these are pseudo-albinos or so-called albinos of the types A and W mentioned in the list of colors given earlier in this chapter. According to Castle, who is our best authority on color in horses, most of the Thompsons' horses are of type W. (See Plate XIIId) This type has the purest white coat and usually, at least, has brown eyes, so that it is generally considered more desirable than the pale ivory, glass-eyed A's, but there is much doubt whether W type can breed absolutely true for color. (In this they differ from other sorts of animals, or from men, that are albinos in the technical sense; these always breed true.)

So far, at least, the club frankly promotes the pseudo- or horse-albino coloring for its own sake and does not stress type. Horses of 14 to 16 hands and 1000 to 1600 pounds are specified, but this includes almost any type except the smallest ponies and largest draft horses. Recent by-laws of the club also allow registration of ponies and draft horses, and so exclude no existing type of horse.

The snow-white type W horses are certainly among the showiest animals on earth. They are, and doubtless will always be, in great demand for rodeos, circuses, parades, and other show purposes. It would be rash to predict whether the color will become popular for pleasure or utility animals or whether a true breed of this color will be, or can be, established.

Part Two

THE LINEAGE OF THE HORSE

10

HUNTERS AND HUNTING OF FOSSIL HORSES

THERE was once a man named William Colchester who lived in Woodbridge 'in the parish of Kingston, commonly called Kyson, in Suffolk,' England. He was a brickmaker, and for his bricks he used to dig clay on the banks of the river Deben near Woodbridge. Sometimes he would dig so deep that he brought up some of the sand that underlay the clay, and then he had to throw this useless sand to one side. One day in the year 1838 he was about to toss away a shovel-full of sand when he noticed in it a small tooth with every appearance of being very ancient.

There was another Englishman named William Richardson, Esq., M.A., F.G.S., who was an enthusiastic naturalist. One day in 1839 he was visiting a place called Studd Hill on the coast of Kent. He found there the remains of many ancient, fossilized plants, and he therefore looked about with, as he said, 'strong expectation for the evidence of some form of animal life, whether of beast or bird, destined to be sustained by so rich a provision.' Luckier than most (for it is not as common as you might think to find the remains of fossil plants and fossil animals together), he soon found a large part of an ancient animal's skull, with most of the teeth well-preserved.

These two incidents did not seem very important at the time. They might have been forgotten long since, and the two Williams, Colchester and Richardson, along with them, except for a fact that no one realized then. What Colchester and Richardson had discovered were the first known remains of the oldest members of the horse family. We still do not know any older than these, although we now know vastly more about these than could be learned in 1838 or 1839. No one even suspected at that time that these were ancestral horses. How could they? The specimens found by Colchester and Richardson had almost no special resemblance to the living horse. The teeth, instead of the great, ridged, grinding prisms of our present horse, were small, low, and cusped, really more like monkey teeth than horse teeth. The little skull, with its relatively large eyes set about midway from snout to ears, instead of far back in the skull as are the relatively small eyes of modern horses, looked (as its first describer, Richard Owen, remarked) rather like 'that of the Hare or other timid Rodentia.' From the evidence then available, it would have been most unscientific to jump to the conclusion that this queer little beast was a sort of horse. Owen named it *Hyracotherium*. (A copy of Owen's illustration of the little skull is given in Plate XIVa.)

Twenty years after these discoveries were made, in 1859, Charles Darwin (Plate XVIc) published a book called in pompous Victorian style, *The Origin of Species by Means of Natural Selection; or, the Preservation of Favored Races in the Struggle for Life*. A great many people before Darwin (including his own grandfather, Erasmus Darwin) had the idea of evolution and believed that species of animals and plants are not immutable creations but develop naturally from older and different species. It was, however, Darwin's great book, which in this less leisurely day we call simply *The Origin of Species,* that backed up this idea with evidence so extensive and so conclusive that the theory of evolution was soon accepted by practically all scientists. With the firm establishment of this theory, students of fossils, that is, paleontologists, naturally began to look around to see whether they could not, by comparing ancient animals of different ages, find the ancestors of living animals.

When Darwin wrote *The Origin of Species* the known fossils were so few and scattered that they provided few good examples of gradual change from one species to another. In fact Darwin had to devote considerable space in his book to proving that the sudden appearance of many species of animals without known ancestors did not necessarily mean that his ideas of gradual change from one species to another were wrong. Men had been curiously searching for fossils for a long time, but now they had a new and important reason for the search. Their most impressive early success was the discovery of a long series of fossil horses. Within twenty years of the publication of *The Origin of Species* the paleontologists were able to demonstrate by a nearly continuous series of intermediate forms that the little animal *Hyracotherium*, found by Colchester and Richardson a generation earlier, which was an English representative of the eohippus group, was the ancestor of our living horse. The fact that it looked so different from a horse in almost every way is simply an example of the profound changes that evolution can bring about in the course of 60 million years or so.

The piecing together of this story has involved the collection of thousands of fossils on every continent except Australia (which never had any native horses) and their study by hundreds of students of many nationalities. The first important step was taken by Thomas Henry Huxley (Plate XIVc), a great naturalist who was one of Darwin's closest friends and most pugnacious defenders—he called himself 'Darwin's bulldog.' (He was, by the way, the grandfather of the novelist Aldous Huxley and of another great student of evolution, Julian Huxley.) In 1872 he pointed out that if four kinds of fossil mammals already known from Europe were placed in their correct order of age they formed a graded series. This series led from an early and primitive creature called *Palaeotherium* through *Anchitherium* and *Hipparion* to fossil *Equus* and so to living *Equus*. He suggested that here might be a real example of the evolution of a living animal through some millions of years of geological time.

In the following year (1873) a Russian paleontologist, Vladimir Kovalevsky (Plate XIVb), studied these fossils in greater detail and came to the same conclusion. A few years later (1876), he stated still more definitely that *Palaeotherium — Anchitherium — Hipparion — Equus* represents the ancestry of the horse. Both he and Huxley realized, however, that there were breaks in the series as it was then known and that the actual gradations between these genera had not been found. Neither of them realized that *Hyracotherium* belongs at the beginning of this series, but Kovalevsky did note that it is related to the early horses.

This early work carried the story almost as far as was possible in Europe. The fact is, as we now know, that the central lines of horse evolution did not occur on that continent. Huxley and Kovalevsky were perfectly right in listing these genera as successive stages of evolution among the relatives of the horses, but the three earlier forms were not directly ancestral to *Equus* and belong on three different offshoots from the direct ancestry. The first was a side branch that evolved in the Old World and the other two had migrated successively from the distant region where direct descent to *Equus* was occurring. This sort of thing happened frequently in the course of evolution and is responsible for series of structural stages which lack the actual ancestral-descendant transitional links. The transition can only be filled in by preservation and discovery of fossils in the region where the main evolutionary line was developing.

Fortunately in the case of the horse this region was found and it proved to be rich in fossils. It was, in fact, the region that is now the United States. Some fossil horses had been found here early in the nineteenth century or perhaps even before that, but they were young as fossils go, belonged to the modern genus *Equus,* and were not always recognized as different from living horses. Around the middle of the last century discoveries were becoming more frequent, and they included a variety of forms older than *Equus* and distinctly different. Most of these, in that period, were described by Joseph Leidy (1823-91, Plate XIVd) of Philadelphia, a great American naturalist who was the first to make extensive and systematic studies of extinct mammals in America. (Many before him, including Thomas Jefferson, who set aside a room in the White House for his collection of fossils, had published briefer and scattered notes on this subject.) In a classic volume published in 1869, Leidy brought together a whole series of American fossil horses.

Leidy actually had several distinct stages in the direct, true ancestry of *Equus* (stages now placed in the genera *Mesohippus, Parahippus,* and *Merychippus*), along with two side-branches related to those that migrated to Europe (*Hypohippus* and *Hipparion*). The time was not yet ripe, however, for realization of their significance—this was even before Huxley and Kovalevsky had noticed the possible evolutionary meaning of the European forms. Leidy recognized that these animals were relatives of the horse, but he did not attempt to use them to reconstruct horse ancestry.

Much has since been filled in, but completion of the discovery of the main stages in the ancestry of *Equus,* and the realization that this is what they are occurred rapidly in the decade after Leidy's publication. This was done in largest part by Othniel Charles Marsh (1831-99, Plate XVa), a professor at Yale University, with some unfriendly assistance from his bitter rival Edward Drinker Cope (1840-97, Plate XVb) of Philadelphia. Marsh made several trips to the western fossil fields himself and he also employed many collectors, who sent great quantities of bones to his laboratories in New Haven. Early forms, unknown to Leidy, allies of the little European *Hyracotherium,* began to come in during 1871 and 1872. During the same period, discoveries in less ancient geological deposits also began to fill in the gaps between the various forms described by Leidy.

As early as 1874 Marsh said of his fossil American horses that 'The line of descent appears to have been direct, and the remains now known supply every important form.' The last part of this sentence was over-optimistic (Marsh himself was to add other highly important forms). Time has, however, confirmed Marsh's belief that he had identified the direct line of descent. During the next few years he worked out some of the more important evolutionary changes in teeth, legs, and feet. (See Fig. 9)

In 1876, Huxley came to America on a lecture tour. One of his lectures was to be on the evolution of the horse, as he and Kovalevsky had worked it out from the European fossils. He spent two days in New Haven going over Marsh's specimens and discussing the conclusions based on them. (See Fig. 10) As a result, Huxley's lecture was hurriedly rewritten and he expounded the theory of the American ancestry of the horse family. It was later in that same year (1876) that Marsh's collectors sent him his first remains of eohippus. He then added this, still the earliest known stage of horse history, to the ancestral series. It was, however, Cope who had described the first

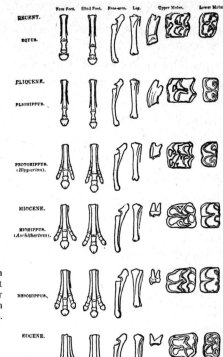

RECENT.	Fore Foot.	Hind Foot.	Fore-arm.	Leg.	Upper Molar.	Lower Molar.
EQUUS.						

9. The genealogy of the horse as known to Marsh and published in 1879. Feet and leg bones and upper and lower teeth are shown in geological succession from bottom to top. Not drawn to scale.

PLIOCENE.
PLIOHIPPUS.

PROTOHIPPUS.
(Hipparion).

MIOCENE.
MIOHIPPUS.
(Anchitherium).

MESOHIPPUS.

EOCENE.
OROHIPPUS.

GENEALOGY OF THE HORSE.

10. 'Eohippus and Eohomo,' sketched by T. H. Huxley. When Huxley visited Marsh in 1876, Marsh persuaded him that eohippus is the ancestor of the horse. Huxley decided that the first horse should have a first rider, and he drew this cartoon as a joke.

Eohippus + Eohomo

American remains of this genus in 1873. It was also Cope, a few years later, who showed that eohippus is the American representative of *Hyracotherium*. Cope thus finally placed the little animals found in England in 1838 and 1839 in their correct position as horse ancestors.

So many people have studied fossil horses since Marsh and Cope that a list of all of them would stretch to impossible length. Any shorter list courts criticism on grounds of favoritism or unfair omissions. Three men will, nevertheless, be mentioned, not only because their studies of fossil horses were among the most important, but also because the men themselves were outstanding among great students of fossil mammals in general during the period between Marsh and Cope and the present. Henry Fairfield Osborn (1857-1935, Plate XVc) directed the assembling at the American Museum of Natural History of the best series of fossil horses now available anywhere. He also made extensive studies of these fossils. The same collection was the basis of important work by Osborn's student, William Diller Matthew (1871-1930, Plate XVIa), who brought the whole story of horse evolution into modern form, modified only in details by his successors. William Berryman Scott (1858-1947, Plate XVIb), of Princeton University, contributed less specifically to the study of fossil horses, but did include some of these in his extensive and basic works on American fossil mammals.

Most of the American and foreign students of fossil mammals— and there have been hundreds of such students—have dealt with fossil horses at one time or another. No less important has been the work of the bonediggers who have found the fossils, collected them, and sent them in for study. Often collector and student have been the same man. Matthew, for instance, collected many of the fossils he described. His close associate Walter Granger (1872-1941), one of the greatest of fossil mammal collectors, described some of his own finds, although he usually preferred to leave this to Matthew. In other cases outstanding collectors and preparers of fossils have been content with these energetic tasks without adding those of identification and description. In the same team with Matthew and Granger, Albert Thomson (1874-1948) was an outstanding example of the highly skilled specialist in finding, collecting, and preparing fossil horses and other mammals.

How do such men set about finding a fossil horse, how did the fossil get there to begin with, and how is it collected? There are many different answers to these questions, for there are many ways and places in which animals become fossilized, and correspondingly different problems in finding and collecting them. Typical methods are shown in Plates XVII-XVIII, and can be made clear by an example:

The year is 1924, the place the Staked Plains of the Texas Panhandle. W. D. Matthew and an eager but clumsy young assistant are prospecting for fossil horses in the blazing sunshine that beats down on the broken country around Mount Blanco. Their procedure is tiring and monotonous. They have no way of knowing where digging will reveal a fossil, except by finding a fossil before they start digging. There is no way of locating a fossil still wholly buried. No dipping wand and no electronic instrument yet invented will reveal its presence. To dig at random would be a hopeless task. Fossils are widely scattered, and a hundred holes might be sunk without hitting one.

So the collectors simply walk along, eyes glued to the ground, systematically looking over the bare exposures of clay and sandstone. Erosion is taking its toll here, eating back into the subsurface of the plains and forming a jumble of ravines and badlands. Each successive storm washes out more of the clay and stone and scatters fragments down the slopes. Among these fragments are bits of fossil bones and teeth, long buried there and now resurrected by erosion. These fragments are the objects of the search. Looking at a distance much like mere chunks of stone, they must be detected by slight differences of color and suggestive peculiarities of form, a bonedigger's knack that seems almost inborn in some and that most can acquire by experience.

Why the collectors are looking just here for fossil horses is a story that goes back some thirty-five years. This is a known fossil field. If it were not, no plan for systematic collecting could have been made. They could know from the general type of rock and geological conditions that fossils *might* occur here—but there is a long pull from that 'might occur' to 'do occur.' The discovery of a fossil field in the first place may be made in many different ways. Often this is a lucky accident. A rancher may come across an odd stone in his pasture and be curious enough to send it to a museum or university. Travelers may pick up curios which eventually come to the attention of someone who recognizes them as possible leads to a fossil field. More systematically, naturalists working in a region for other reasons often keep their eyes open for fossils, and sometimes come across the first clue to important finds. Geologists particularly, studying the general structure and rock distribution in a region, always have an eye out for fossils and often locate new deposits.

This fossil field near Mount Blanco was discovered in the last-mentioned way. In the winter of 1889-90, W. F. Cummins was examining the geology of the Staked Plains for the Texas Geological Survey. He ran across a few fragments of fossil mammals in this area and sent them to be identified by the famous paleontologist E. D. Cope—the Cope whose pioneer studies of fossil horses supplemented those of Marsh, as mentioned above. Although then nearing the end of his career (he died in 1897), Cope was still an active man in his fifties. He was so much interested in the fossils sent by Cummins that he was anxious to visit the spot and to collect more of them. In 1892 the Texas Survey made this possible by employing him to explore in the Panhandle with Cummins. The discoveries that Cope made at that time showed that this was indeed an important new fossil field with a variety of hitherto unknown animals, although the field is rather small in area.

Among the fossils found by Cope were some horse teeth of a distinctive type that he named *Equus simplicidens*. Later collectors found some more fragments of this species, but only fragments, and it remained very poorly known. Matthew recognized that this represented an important stage in the rise of *Equus* from its immediate ancestors and was anxious to learn more about the transition. He therefore decided to spend part of the 1924 field season on the Blanco beds (so named for the near-by landmark, Mount Blanco), search-

ing for better specimens of this horse and of the animals that lived
with it.

After some days of prospecting, Matthew came to a place where
several promising bits of bone were scattered down the slope. There
was some chance that these were parts of a skeleton just starting to
weather out. In that case, it might be possible to find other bones,
perhaps most of the skeleton, still buried and not all broken up or
washed away. He therefore worked up the slope carefully on hands
and knees, picking up each piece of bone as he went. When no more
scraps were found on the surface, he knew that the buried bones, if
any remained, must be at or a little above this level. Looking about
with even greater care, he saw with joy that there were indeed some
bone ends sticking out of the uneroded white clay.

With a small one-handed pick he cut back the clay above the
bones. Then, working with great care not to disturb the fragile and
badly cracked fossil bones, he exposed them bit by bit, using small
awls to work away the clay immediately around them. As this was
loosened, it was brushed away with whiskbroom or smaller dust
brushes. The bones tended to go to pieces as they were exposed, so
they were hardened little by little with thin shellac. When this had
dried, as it did very quickly in the hot, dry Texas air, the bone
surface was further protected and the fragments held together by
covering with absorbent rice paper and another coating of shellac.

In a couple of days the whole specimen was exposed, shellacked,
and papered on top. With delight, Matthew noted that it was exactly
what he most wanted to find: a skeleton of Cope's horse (*Equus simplicidens*), known until then only from a few separate teeth. There
was, however, one bitter disappointment. The skeleton was practically complete, all but the most important part, the head. This had
been weathered out and its fragments had been washed away beyond
recovery. In the meantime, Matthew's assistant had been prospecting
up a near-by draw, hoping to make some discovery to rival the boss's.
He, too, found a lead to a partly buried fossil and breathlessly
worked in to see what he had. Soon he was running back to Matthew, wild with excitement. He had a horse skeleton, too, a much
less complete skeleton in all but one respect: his had the head still

there! It was his first important discovery and the high point of his budding career. (No wonder I remember it so vividly a quarter of a century later!)

How these skeletons came to be preserved there and to be discovered was by a chance so small that it seems almost a miracle. Of the uncounted billions of animals that have lived on the earth, extremely few have become fossils. To become fossilized, the bones must, first of all, be buried. The great majority of dead animals lie on the surface of the ground, where their remains are scattered by scavengers and eventually molder away to unrecognizable dust. A few may sink in mud or quicksand, where death and burial are simultaneous. Scattered bones and teeth may occasionally be drifted over by windblown dust or washed into streams and buried in sand bars or in the mud spread by floods. Only these bones buried before decay have any chance of preservation as fossils, but even among them only a minute number become available to bonediggers of today.

The chemistry of the deposit must be such that the mineral matter of the bones is not dissolved but is preserved or replaced. The bones must remain buried from a time shortly after death, perhaps millions of years ago, up to recent times. Many deposits of winds, lakes, streams, or seas in which bones may be buried are washed away again in a few centuries or millennia. Then their fossils are usually completely lost, for even well-petrified bones readily go to pieces when exposed to air and to the forces of erosion. For recovery, a fossil deposit must remain well buried for just the right length of time, and then must again be near the surface and partly exposed by erosion within a short time before a bonedigger happens to come along. Small wonder that there are deficiencies in the fossil record. When you consider this series of chances it is wonderful that the record is not all gaps!

In the case of the horse skeletons found by Matthew and his assistant, the long shot had come off at odds far greater than in any race to be run by these horses' descendants. The animals had wandered to the edge of a shallow pond on the grassy plains of Texas a million years ago, more or less. There they had died—why does not appear. They do not seem to have bogged down, and killing by

wolves or big cats would probably have been followed by dismem-
berment. Perhaps they had eaten poisonous plants and died here
while quenching thirst. In any event, die they did. Their flesh decayed, but their bones sank into the soft mud along the margin of
the pond. Freshets washed fresh layers of sand and mud over the
deposit until the skeletons were deeply buried. Pressure and time
turned the soft sands and muds into sandstone and hard, shaly
clay. Eventually with changes in climate and in level, intermittent
streams began to eat back into the edges of the high plains. The
small basin filled with sediment so long ago was again exposed. Only
a year or two, probably, before 1924, erosion had reached the edges
of these buried skeletons and storms had begun to wash them out
from their long secure burial place. Matthew and his assistant had
the luck to find them at just this critical time and, working with
greater care and purpose, they completed the exposure started by
the blind forces of nature.

If the bones had been removed simply by digging out each one
and picking it up, they would have been badly broken and their relationships to each other would have been lost. It was decided to take
them back to New York in blocks of clay, just as they were buried.
There in the laboratory they could be removed and cleaned without damage during the following winter months. A trench was dug
around each skeleton, just touching the bones all around and
leaving the skeleton exposed on the top of a low pillar. Then burlap
sacking was cut into strips. The strips were soaked one by one in
flour paste and worked down with finger tips over the bones and
the clay around them until the whole pillar, top and sides, was
encased. (Plaster is better for this, but these collectors did not have
available any quick-setting plaster and in a dry climate flour paste
will do.) For added strength, sticks were laid across the block as
splints and fastened in place with additional flour paste and burlap
bandages.

When this casing was thoroughly dry, the pillar was undercut
and small tunnels were carefully dug under the block. Through
these, bandages were run as cinches, to keep the cracked clay and
bones from falling out when the block was rolled over. This

turning, the most crucial part of the whole operation, was successfully performed and the bones moved for the first time in a million years or so. Then the bottom, now turned up, was also trimmed down to the bone, shellacked, papered, and bandaged. Each block was then ready for the trip to town, for packing in wooden boxes there, and for shipment to New York.

In New York each block was opened and the bones were slowly removed, cleaned, hardened, and restored by skillful preparators. Then the bones were assembled as in the living animal and mounted on iron supports. The two skeletons were of the same species and the same size, so the more nearly complete skeleton, Matthew's discovery, was mounted and a plaster cast of the skull from the other skeleton was used to complete it. After months of labor, the reconstructed skeleton was placed on display at the American Museum of Natural History, where it is still exhibited.

Each story is different, but every one of the thousands of discoveries of fossil horses, from fragments of teeth to whole skeletons, has back of it some such tale as that. The long search for fossil horses has been exceptionally successful, and their known remains now give a relatively complete and nearly continuous history.

11

TIME-SCALE OF HORSE HISTORY

THE history of the horse as a domestic animal covers some 4,000 years, a respectable period but only a fleeting instant in comparison with the history of the horse family as a whole. To study this larger history, we need some sort of dating system and our human historical B.C. and A.D. will not do. The method that has been devised for this purpose has a different basis; it designates the sequence in which events occurred and not the number of years that have elapsed. Dating by sequence is a simple and effective system. American history could be studied this way. For instance, if we knew only the succession of Presidents and not how long each served, we still could follow events sufficiently well for most purposes. We should know that events of the Washington epoch were considerably earlier than those of the Lincoln epoch or, on a finer scale, that the latter part of Term 1 of Franklin D. Roosevelt came before his early Term 2. For many purposes it would not matter at all whether we knew the dates in years.

This sort of method is applied by geologists to the history of the earth. A broad sequence of major time divisions has been established and within each one of these there are subdivisions, successively smaller, in established succession. The various divisions and subdivisions have been given more or less arbitrary names, a system more flexible and, as a rule, easier to remember than, for instance, the use of numbers or letters.

The largest divisions of geologic time are called eras, and five of these are usually recognized: Archaeozoic, Proterozoic, Paleozoic, Mesozoic, and Cenozoic, in order from earliest to latest. No fossils

are surely known from the Archaeozoic and only a few from the Proterozoic. Fossils are abundant thereafter. The first vertebrates (animals with back-bones), fish-like aquatic forms, appeared during the
first half of the Paleozoic and later in that era some of them evolved
into four-footed types, amphibians at first and later reptiles. Mammals and birds, the last major sorts of vertebrates to arise, both appeared during the first half of the Mesozoic but were rare until after
the close of that era.

The Cenozoic is characterized by abundant mammals and is
often called the Age of Mammals. (The last part of it is sometimes
separated as the Age of Man, but man is a mammal, too.) Mammals
that may be definitely placed in the horse family first appeared
some time after the beginning of the Cenozoic and the whole history
of the family occurred during that era. To follow this history, it is
necessary to use subdivisions of the Cenozoic as dates, and it will
save time if you will now learn the right hand column of Fig. 11.
You can then follow the story (not only of the horse but, in wider
reading, of most other mammals and of your own mammalian
ancestry) without stopping to think each time whether an Oligocene
horse is earlier or later than an Eocene horse and without my
wasting space and abusing your patience by explaining this each
time. Do not bother to learn the column second from right. These
are names for still smaller subdivisions included so that you will
have them for reference and to help if you want to go on from this
book to more detailed studies of fossils. The names in the last column are used and applied all over the world, but those in the
next to last column are applied only to North America.

Everyone would like to put this relative or sequential time scale
on an absolute basis. For most studies it is enough to know that
Eocene is older than Oligocene, for instance, but it would greatly
increase the value of some studies to know precisely how long the
Eocene or Oligocene was. It would also add enormously to the
interest of the story, both for the scientist and for the layman. Age
in years cannot yet be determined exactly enough to be of much use
in technical studies or to replace the relative scale, but we do have
some idea of it.

EXAMPLES OF FOSSIL DEPOSITS	TYPICAL HORSE	PROVINCIAL AGE	EPOCH
			RECENT
			PLEISTOCENE
Blanco	Equus Plesippus?	BLANCAN	PLIOCENE OR PLEISTOCENE
Hemphill	Pliohippus	HEMPHILLIAN	PLIOCENE
Valentine		CLARENDONIAN	
Barstow	Merychippus	BARSTOVIAN	MIOCENE
Sheep Creek		HEMINGFORDIAN	
Harrison	Parahippus	ARIKAREEAN	
Brulé	Miohippus	WHITNEYAN	OLIGOCENE
		ORELLAN	
Chadron	Mesohippus	CHADRONIAN	
Duchesne River	Epihippus	DUCHESNIAN	EOCENE
Uinta		UINTAN	
Bridger	Orohippus	BRIDGERIAN	
Willwood	Eohippus	WASATCHIAN	
Tiffany	(No Horses) Ectoconus (a Condylarth)	TIFFANIAN	PALEOCENE
Torrejon		TORREJONIAN	
		PUERCAN	
CRETACEOUS PERIOD — END OF THE AGE OF REPTILES			

11. The geologic time scale of horse history. Only the last 70 to 75 million years of earth history (the Cenozoic Era) are shown. The scale runs from oldest, below, to younger, above. The scenes at the left are actual localities in western United States where fossil mammals, including horses, of the given age have been found.

The best information is obtained from certain minerals containing radioactive elements, such as uranium. These elements break down into others, with lead as one of the end products, at an invariable and determinable rate. By measuring how far the breakdown has gone, it is possible to learn how long it has been going on and thus how old the mineral in question is. Suitable minerals are not too common and there are various technical difficulties, so that only a few really reliable determinations have yet been made. One of these few fortunately belongs somewhere near where students of horse history would most like to have a year date, toward the beginning of the Tertiary and at about the time when the horse family first appears in the fossil record. This date is approximately 60 million years ago (even the best determinations are not accurate within a few per cent).

Unfortunately, another difficulty arises in this case. We know, within a certain margin of error, that this particular mineral is about 60 million years old, but we are not quite sure what its age is on the geological sequence-scale. Some students consider it as of early Paleocene age, which would make the Tertiary begin at about that date. The horse family record begins at the beginning of the Eocene and this dating would, with some guess work, place that event as 45 to 50 million years ago. Other students, however, say that this particular mineral is from the end, not the beginning, of the Paleocene. In that case, the horse record began about 60 million years ago and the Tertiary began considerably earlier, perhaps 70 or 75 million years ago. At the present writing, this dating seems more likely to be correct.

Undoubtedly other more suitable radioactive minerals will be found and methods will be improved so that the year dating can be made more accurate and reliable. In the meantime, it is a great deal to know, without much serious doubt, that the horse pedigree to be sketched later in this chapter covers something on the order of 45 to 60 million years.

Even less is known about the lengths in years of the various epochs included in this span. It is agreed that they are of unequal lengths. The Recent is usually taken to cover only the last 20 or 30 thousand years—a very short time comparatively. The Pleistocene perhaps accounts for 1 million years; some say as little as 500 thousand and some as much as 2 million. The Tertiary epochs must all have been much longer than this, averaging 10 to 15 million years apiece. The Eocene was probably the longest of these epochs and the Oligocene or Pliocene the shortest. The Eocene may have been as much as twice as long as either of these latter epochs. The Miocene was apparently of intermediate length. As a series of rough but reasoned guesses, the dates and lengths of the various Cenozoic epochs may then be more or less as follows:

Epoch	Date at which epoch may have begun (in years before the present)	Approximate duration of epoch (in years)	Relative lengths of epochs
Recent	25 thousand	25 thousand	$\frac{1}{400}$
Pleistocene	1 million	1 million	$\frac{1}{10}$
Pliocene	10 million	10 million	1
Miocene	25 million	15 million	$1\frac{1}{2}$
Oligocene	35 million	10 million	1
Eocene	55 million	20 million	2
Paleocene	$72\frac{1}{2}$ million	$17\frac{1}{2}$ million	$1\frac{3}{4}$

12

FORERUNNERS OF THE HORSES

HORSES have had ancestors as long as anybody. It is possible that life has arisen more than once on the earth, but this is not probable. Every animal or plant now living has a tremendously long line of ancestors, and from this point of view all of them are of equal antiquity, going back more than a billion years for every organism of today, whether ameba or man. The horse ancestry, along with our own and that of all present day animals, probably started with some one-celled microscopic ameba-like organism, and perhaps even earlier with a still smaller virus-like living molecule. There is, unfortunately, no fossil record of these very earliest stages. Much later the ancestral branch that was to lead to horses, men, and other higher forms had evolved into many-celled aquatic animals with a stiff rod (notochord) down the back, forerunner of the jointed (vertebrate) backbone. These creatures were fish-like, but they had no jaws and were more primitive than fishes in other ways as well. From them true fishes arose and then from one line of fishes there evolved four-footed animals able to walk on land. Some of the earliest of these, amphibians, gave rise to early reptiles and finally some reptiles evolved into warm-blooded, milk-giving, hairy animals— the mammals.

This complaint has been lodged against paleontologists: 'Some of you say that man is descended from a monkey-like creature, others that we come from reptiles, and others that our ancestors were fishes. Why can't you get together and stop confusing us?' The answer is that all these statements are true. It depends on how far back in your ancestry you care to go. It should be no more confusing that mankind is descended from fishes, reptiles, and ancient monkey-like forms, among others at different times, than that an individual is descended from his great-grandfather, grandfather, and father. The ancestry of the horse, too, is not just a matter of descent from eohippus, the dawn horse of the Eocene, but goes back through all these earlier and distinctly non-horselike stages.

For the hundreds of millions of years up to the time when mammals arose (on the order of 150 million years ago) and during the first half, more or less, of the history of mammals, the ancestry of horses and of men was the same. The same fishes, the same amphibians, the same reptiles, and the same early mammals were destined to give rise to both horses and men. We are blood relatives of the horse, and rather close relatives when the whole of the animal kingdom is compared. Man is, for instance, more closely related to the horse than is the opossum, much closer than is a lizard, and incomparably closer than is a clam.

The relationship may not seem very close on our human time scale, however. The last common ancestor of man and horse probably lived in the Cretaceous period, before the Age of Mammals, at least 75 and perhaps 100 million years ago. Since then the lines leading to men and to horses have been distinct and have evolved in radically different ways, but without obliterating many similarities in our skeletons and other anatomical features, even including the brain.

Here there are several stages of horse—or, really, of pre-horse—history that are not well recorded by fossils so far discovered. The ancestry of the horses has been traced back almost continuously to eohippus. Although, as will be shown, eohippus was very unlike the modern horse, it is placed in the horse family, Equidae. Before eohippus there is a break. Bonediggers have not, as yet, had the good fortune to find the precise immediate ancestors of eohippus or those that would show exactly where and when the horse family first arose. Eohippus lived in the early Eocene, and its ancestry cannot now be clearly followed back through the Paleocene or into the Cretaceous.

The general group of earlier mammals from which the Equidae arose is known, even though the exact line of descent has not yet been traced. The characters of the immediate forerunners of eohippus can thus be demonstrated with little doubt in a general way although not in complete detail. This ancestral group is the Order Condylarthra (con-dye-lar'-thra), a primitive stock long extinct as such, but surviving, in greatly altered form, in the sense that it was the source not only of the horses but also of most or all of the later and recent hoofed mammals. Condylarths first appear in the fossil record at the beginning of the Paleocene, and they were the typical and abundant herbivores throughout that epoch. They lived on into the Eocene, and *Phenacodus* (fen-ack'-o-duss), an early Eocene contemporary of eohippus, is now the best-known of condylarths. (See Plate XIX) In the Eocene they were in competition with more progressive animals derived from their own earlier stock. They failed in this competition and died out before the end of the Eocene.

The condylarths are so important for an understanding of the history of mammals in general and of horses in particular that it will pay us to consider them in a little more detail. They had characters suggestive of both carnivores and hoofed herbivores (ungulates). The latter condylarths were evolving more in the direction of the ungulates, but some early forms can hardly be distinguished from early carnivores to such a point as to suggest that carnivores and ungulates are all of common origin at around this time (early Paleocene). It may be, indeed, that the lion and the lamb are cousins.

Condylarths similar to *Phenacodus*, which represent the sort of animal believed to be ancestral to the horse family, still had some suggestion of the carnivore about them. The rather long and low, rangy body with a small head and long, stout tail was remotely dog-like, or, at least, as much dog-like as horse-like. The feet were padded, as in the dogs, with wrist and heel held somewhat, but not far, off the ground. Each foot had five toes, the primitive number for mammals. (Man is a primitive mammal in this, as in some other respects.) The weight was carried by the second to fourth toes and the third (middle) toe was stoutest and longest, with the first and fifth reduced in size. In some condylarths the toes terminated in structures intermediate between claws and hooves, but in *Phenaco-*

dus, and doubtless also in the ancestors of the Equidae, each toe bore a separate small hoof.

Upper and lower leg segments were of nearly equal lengths, a fact which suggests that the animals were not very fleet runners. The bones of the lower legs (radius and ulna in the lower front leg or 'fore-arm,' tibia and fibula in the lower hind leg or shin) were all stout, unreduced and unfused. There was considerable flexibility in each leg, and they were not yet rigidly specialized for fore-and-aft running motion, as they were to become in the horses and some other groups. This flexibility was retained in most carnivores but lost in most ungulates.

The wrist (carpus) and to less extent the ankle (tarsus) bones had a curious and rather puzzling peculiarity. Each toe tended to be supported by a single, separate wrist or ankle bone, and in the wrist the bones of the second, upper row tended to lie directly above the bones of the lower row. The arrangement looks mechanically defective, as if strong stresses, as in jumping, would tend to split the toes and wrist bones apart, producing serious sprains or permanent crippling. The arrangement probably was not as weak as it looks, but can hardly have been as strong as in most later ungulates, including the horses, in which the stresses are effectively spread by overlapping between the various rows of bones. Some students take this distinction between the serial condylarth carpus and the alternating higher ungulate carpus so seriously that they question whether condylarths could really have given rise to horses and other progressive ungulates. There is, however, no obvious reason why the serial carpus could not have evolved into the alternating type. Indeed, in the horse family and some other groups the alternating arrangement was not ideal in the earlier forms and was gradually perfected as time went on.

The condylarth skull was also very primitive and suggests that of a fully generalized, unspecialized mammal. The most peculiar thing about it is that it has so few peculiarities. The eye, of moderate size, was almost in the middle of the skull so that the snout, neither reduced as it is in us nor elongated as it is in the modern horse, was about as long as the cranium. The orbit (eye-socket) was open behind and not closed by a bony bar as it is in men and in modern horses.

From the proportions of the cranium we know that the brain was relatively small, and from casts of the interior of the cranium, which roughly reproduce the brain that once occupied this space, we know that the brain was low in type. The animals had rather good sensory equipment, especially as regards the sense of smell, but they were low in brain areas devoted to more intellectual processes, to 'thinking things over.' In fact, condylarths must have been extremely stupid in comparison with modern horses (let alone men).

Condylarths had, on each side in both upper and lower jaws, 3 incisors, 1 canine, 4 premolars, and 3 molars, a total of 11 teeth in each jaw (left and right, upper and lower) or 44 teeth in all. This is the primitive number for all mammals except a few that branched off much earlier, during the Mesozoic era. Most of the more specialized later mammals show some reduction by loss of teeth. We humans, for instance, are somewhat specialized in this respect and normally have 2 incisors, 1 canine, 2 premolars, and 3 molars on each side, above and below, or a total of 32—12 less than the primitive number. The third molar ('wisdom tooth') is variable in us and sometimes does not function at all, and in some human families there is a hereditary absence of one of the two normal incisors, suggesting that there is a tendency for man's dentition to be still further reduced.

The condylarth dentition was also primitive in that the teeth were in nearly continuous series, with no very large gaps or diastemata (singular, diastema). We have no diastemata, but all horses do, even eohippus. The condylarth incisors were small, simple, pointed teeth. In *Phenacodus* the canine teeth were somewhat enlarged and doglike, but in some other condylarths they were small, resembling the incisors, and this probably was the condition in the ancestor of eohippus. In the upper jaw, the first two premolars were simple, with only one main point or cusp, but the third and fourth (last two) premolars were triangular and had a distinct inner cusp. (By 'inner' we mean on the tongue or lingual side, as opposed to the outer, cheek, or buccal side of a tooth.) The upper molars were also basically triangular with two main outer and one main inner cusp, but the first two molars were somewhat squared by the addition of a second, smaller inner cusp behind the first. The lower cheek teeth, that is, premolars and molars together, were also progressively more complicated from the simple first premolar to the rather complex first molar. The three molars had similar patterns, with five main cusps, and vestiges of a sixth, arranged in a characteristic way seen in the accompanying illustration (Fig. 12).

These condylarth teeth all had low crowns and if subjected to heavy wear would not have lasted very long. The various cusps on the cheek teeth were fairly distinct, with little tendency to merge into crests. Both of these characteristics are also primitive for ungulates in general and both, incidentally, are also seen in the human dentition, which is rather primitive in spite of its reduction in number of teeth. Such teeth serve adequately for holding and crushing food, but are poor for cutting or grinding. They strongly suggest that most condylarths were not yet fully herbivorous but were omnivorous, eating almost any succulent food, animal or vegetable, that came their way—much as we tend to do with our somewhat similar teeth, unless we persuade ourselves that some sorts of food are not good for us or are not ethical.

Such was the group of animals from which the horses and other hoofed herbivores arose. Knowledge of them places us in a position to judge what the peculiarities of eohippus and other early horses mean and why their rise started new lines of evolution, lines destined to culminate in *Equus*. The story of this lineage will start with the little eohippus, but before beginning the account of that animal it will be useful to give, for reference purposes, an outline of all the sorts of fossil horses to be considered. Most of these are so different from the living horses that they have to be classified in different genera. They have no popular names that are precise enough for our purposes. 'Three-toed horse,' for instance, might refer to a great variety of decidedly different sorts of animals through most of the history of the horse family. It is necessary, therefore, to use the scientific system of naming and classifying animals already explained in chapter 1. All the fossil horses are classified into species, of course, but there are so many of these species, and the differences between

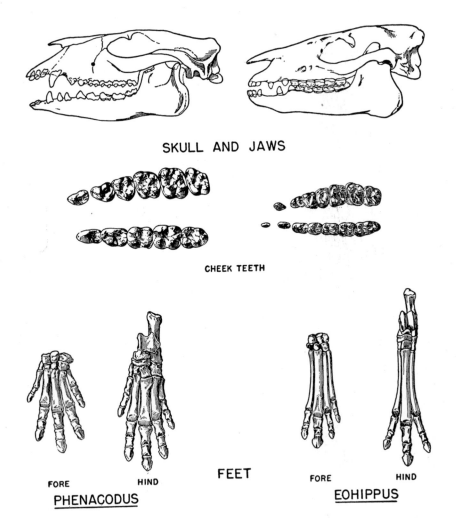

SKULL AND JAWS

CHEEK TEETH

FEET

FORE   HIND   FORE   HIND
PHENACODUS   EOHIPPUS

12. Comparison of a condylarth, *Phenacodus* (left), and a primitive horse, eohippus (right). Both upper and lower cheek teeth (premolars and molars) are shown. Brought to common size, not true relative scale, for comparison; eohippus averages smaller than *Phenacodus*.

them are often so slight, that it would be a waste of time to talk about species in a general account.

The genera of horses, living and fossil, as usually recognized by conservative students today will be listed. Do not bother to read the list through at this point or to try to learn it. The various genera are mentioned in due course on later pages. This list is only for your possible convenience when you have read more, to refer back to and see how the various sorts of ancient horses line up as a whole.

At first sight these names look rather difficult and forbidding, but this is only because they are unfamiliar. No one thinks that 'hippopotamus' is a particularly hard word, and this is, in fact, a technical generic name coined from Greek, just like most of the names of horse genera. The pronunciation of each of these horse names is given on later pages as each is discussed, and by trying them over two or three times it will be found that they are no harder than many common words that adults use all the time. None of these names is longer than the word 'impossibility' and none is as bad a tongue-twister as 'necessarily.'

The names are coined from Greek words, except *Equus* which is simply Latin for 'horse.' *Hippos* is Greek for 'horse,' and you will notice that this root in one form or another occurs in almost all the generic names for extinct horses: Oro-*hippus,* *Hipp*-arion, Nann-*ippus,* and so on. When a new genus is discovered, the first person to publish a description of it has to invent a name for it. He can use any name he wants, as long as the name has never been applied to any other sort of animal. A common practice is to make up names from Greek or Latin, and this was done with all the horse genera. As a rule, the author tries to use words that are more or less appropriate for the animal he is naming, but this is not required. Once a name is given, it *means* the animal to which it is given, and the original meaning of its Greek, Latin, or other roots has no bearing on the case. The roots in *Hyracotherium* mean 'the hyrax-like animal,' but the word *Hyracotherium* means a particular sort of Eocene horse regardless of the fact that it was not really much like a hyrax. *Archaeohippus* is coined from Greek words for 'ancient' and 'horse,' but *Archaeohippus* is not the only ancient horse, or the most ancient.

If you know somebody named, say, George Fletcher, you do not stop to think that his name means 'a farmer who makes arrows.' In fact it does *not* mean that as you use the name: it really means a particular person of your acquaintance, who is probably not a farmer and pretty surely never made an arrow. In the same way, the scientific names of animals *mean* the animals. It becomes simply confusing and gives you twice as much to remember if you stop to think 'Hyracotherium, the hyrax-like beast,' and so on. It is handy to spot the fact that names with 'hippus,' or the like, in them are likely to refer to horses, but do not rely much even on this. A hippopotamus, for instance, is not a horse in spite of the fact that its name is from Greek words meaning 'river horse.'

The technical classification of the genera of horses and the ages and places from which they are known are as follows:

FAMILY EQUIDAE
SUBFAMILY HYRACOTHERIINAE
GENERA:

Hyracotherium. (These are the animals popularly called 'eohippus.')
Known from the early Eocene of North America and Europe.
Orohippus. Middle Eocene of North America.
Epihippus. Late Eocene of North America.

SUBFAMILY ANCHITHERIINAE
GENERA:

Mesohippus. Early and middle Oligocene of North America.
Miohippus. Middle and late Oligocene of North America.
Parahippus. Early to late Miocene of North America.
Archaeohippus. Early to late Miocene of North America.
Anchitherium. Early to middle Miocene of North America and middle to late Miocene of Europe and Asia.
Hypohippus. Early Miocene to early Pliocene of North America and early Pliocene of Asia.
Megahippus. Early Pliocene of North America.

SUBFAMILY EQUINAE
GENERA:

Merychippus. Middle to late Miocene of North America.
Hipparion. Early to late Pliocene of North America, Europe, Asia, and Africa.
Stylohipparion. Pliocene and Pleistocene of Africa.
Neohipparion. Early to late Pliocene of North America.
Nannippus. Early to late Pliocene of North America.
Calippus. Early Pliocene of North America.
Pliohippus. Early to middle Pliocene of North America.
Hippidion. Pleistocene of South America.

[*Continued on next page.*

SUBFAMILY EQUINAE
   GENERA:

Onohippidium. Pleistocene of South America.

Parahipparion. Pleistocene of South America.

Equus. Late Pliocene or Pleistocene to Recent of Europe, Asia, and Africa. Late Pliocene (?) and Pleistocene of North America. Pleistocene of South America. World-wide now in the form of the domestic horse.

13

THE LITTLE EOHIPPUS

ALMOST everyone has heard of little eohippus, the dawn horse. Its name can be found in most dictionaries and has become a part of our common English speech. Unfortunately, it turns out that *Eohippus* is not its correct scientific name and that it should technically be called *Hyracotherium* (hie-rack'-o-thee'-ree-um)—a jaw-breaker that is not likely to win so many friends. This unfortunate situation arose in this way: When Richard Owen came to study the little animals found by the two Williams (see the beginning of chapter 10), he did not recognize that it was ancestral to our horse. No one could have, at that time. The animals are very different throughout and the intermediate stages were not yet known. So Owen compared the small Eocene mammal with the hyraxes (also called klipdasses or conies), the 'feeble folk' of Biblical lore, which, indeed, it resembles more than it does the recent horses. He named it *Hyracotherium,* 'the hyrax-like beast,' a reasonable name although unfortunate in the light of later developments.

When, much later, similar fossils were found in the Eocene of North America, the principle of evolution had been well established and many intermediate forms between this stage and *Equus* were already known. Professor Marsh was therefore able to recognize that these fossils were horse ancestors, and he coined for them the apt and euphonious name *Eohippus,* 'dawn horse,' referring also to the fact that they occur in the Eocene, 'dawn of the recent,' epoch. It was, of course, recognized that *Eohippus* and *Hyracotherium* were close relatives, but the specimens of *Hyracotherium* were all in Europe, those of *Eohippus* were in North America, and without exten-

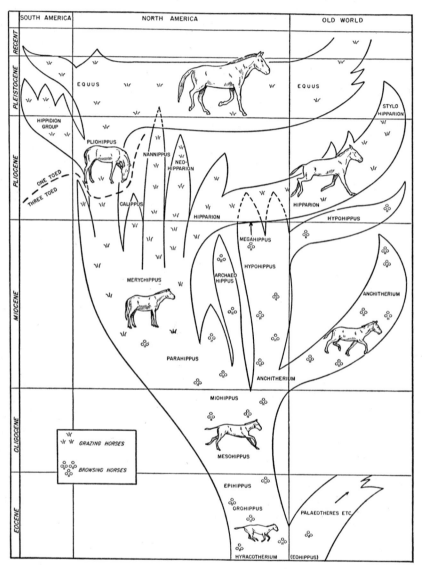

13. The lineages of the horse family. The main lines of horse descent and relationships of the more important genera treated in the text. The restorations are to scale.

sive, first-hand comparison most students supposed that they were related but distinct genera, each characteristic of its own continent. Finally in 1932 the late Sir Clive Forster Cooper was able to make an adequate comparison, and he concluded that *Hyracotherium* and *Eohippus* are so extremely similar that they cannot reasonably be separated generically but must both go under one name. *Hyracotherium* is much the older name of the two and so, under the rules of zoological nomenclature, this is the correct name to use. (In 1947, shortly before his death, Sir Clive enabled me to repeat and to extend his comparisons in the British Museum, Natural History, of which he was then director; my studies fully confirmed his conclusion and put it on a still stronger basis.)

This is all very well, and in our technical studies we have no choice in the matter, but it seems silly to cashier a name as appropriate and as widely known as *Eohippus*. For this reason I propose to keep the name as the common or vernacular equivalent of *Hyracotherium,* and I have used it throughout this book, writing it 'eohippus' and not *Eohippus,* to show that it is used as the common and not as the technical name. (There are good precedents for this procedure. For instance, the peculiar egg-laying, duck-billed mammal of Australia is usually given the common name 'platypus' from a widely used technical name that had to give way to the older and correct scientific name *Ornithorhynchus.*)

What's in a name? Well, at any rate this story reflects interesting side lights on the history of discovery and study, and it emphasizes an important fact: eohippus, earliest known member of the horse family, lived at the same time in both Europe and North America. In both places it appeared at the very beginning of the Eocene. In fact, its appearance is used to help define and recognize the commencement of that epoch. It had no direct ancestors on either continent, so far as we know, and its sudden appearance is part of a dramatic and mysterious episode in the history of life.

During the Paleocene many mammals occurred in both North America and Europe, but most of them were of archaic type, representing ancient offshoots from the ancestry of later mammals but including few of the actual ancestors. Around the end of the Paleo-

cene and beginning of the Eocene, more progressive mammals began
to appear on these continents, many of them more nearly related
to our higher types of modern mammals and some of them, such as
eohippus, directly ancestral to some of these. There was apparently
a simultaneous invasion of the two continents by efficient, forward-
looking mammals coming from—where? No one knows. A popular
hypothesis is that they came from central Asia. Perhaps they did, but
discoveries of fossils in central Asia have not really borne this out,
and there is not a scrap of positive evidence for this or any other
hypothesis. The origin of the progressive late Paleocene and early
Eocene invaders remains one of the enigmas of the history of life.

Wherever it came from, eohippus was an active, abundant, and
highly successful little animal once it reached its new stamping
grounds. In Europe there are no really good collecting fields of early
Eocene age and fossils are few, but eohippus forms a considerable
percentage of those that are known. In the richer early Eocene beds
of North America especially those of the Bighorn Basin in northern
Wyoming and the San Juan Basin in northwestern New Mexico,
eohippus is an abundant fossil. Hundreds, probably thousands, of
specimens have been found, although most of them are fragmentary,
single teeth or scraps of jaws and other bones. For some reason not
clear to me, common as eohippus remains are, it is most unusual
to find so much as a whole skull, and skeletons anywhere near complete are exceedingly rare. As far as I know, only four skeletons have
ever been reconstructed and mounted, although this is a prize that
almost all museums would like to obtain.

Eohippus must have been an attractive little animal. (See Plate XX)
Students have often remarked what a charming pet this little horse
would make. (But they probably think of it as a miniature *Equus*
and would be disappointed in a pet so extremely stupid that it probably could not be trained at all.) There were different species of
eohippus and they varied greatly in size, some being about twice as
large and probably around eight times as heavy as others. The smallest species could not have been much if any over 10 inches high at
the shoulders in a full-grown animal, but other species reached about
20 inches. In modern horsemen's terms, the various eohippuses stood

2:2 to 5 hands. The larger species of eohippus were not particularly tiny animals: they were about half the size of a Shetland pony.

Eohippus had a mixture of primitive characters, suggesting the condylarths, and of incipient specializations, prophetic of the later and more typical horses. On the whole, the primitive characters predominate and eohippus was considerably more like a condylarth than like *Equus*. (See Fig. 12) The back was arched and flexible with, as yet, no hint of the perfectly straight, rigid backbone of a well-formed modern horse. The tail was still long and stout—in *Equus* the tail is short although it may appear long from the hair whisk at the end. The hindquarters were high, giving the animals a strikingly un-horse-like, almost rabbit-like appearance in connection with the arched back.

The long bones of the feet (metacarpals and metatarsals) were relatively longer than in primitive condylarths, carrying the wrist and ankle (knee and hock of domestic horse terminology) farther from the ground, but the elongation and straightening of this part of the leg were less pronounced than in later horses. In the forearm and shin, the ulna and the fibula were still stout and separate from the radius and the tibia respectively, but the articulations with wrist and ankle were not as flexible as in the condylarths.

The toes had already been reduced from the primitive and condylarth number of five. On the front foot there were four toes, each ending in a separate small hoof. These were the second to fifth toes of the original set, the first (outer) toe being completely lost without, as far as has been established, leaving even a vestige. The third toe was largest and longest, the second and fourth equal to each other and somewhat smaller than the third but still fully functional. The fifth toe was considerably smaller, but also functional. Equally remarkable as a difference from *Equus* is the fact that the foot still had a dog-like pad on which, rather than on the hooves themselves, the main weight was carried. The hind foot also had a pad but had only three functional toes, the second to fourth of the original set. As in the front foot, the third toe is largest and the second and fourth are somewhat smaller and equal to each other. The first and fifth toes are completely lost as far as any use of them is concerned, but are believed to be represented by tiny nubbins of bone articulated in the appropriate positions on the ankle bones.

The skull of eohippus was still very condylarth-like. (See Fig. 12) The large eye is still set in the middle of the skull (from front to back), the orbit is still open behind, and the snout is still no longer than the brain case. These proportions are so different from *Equus* that the head of eohippus, when correctly restored, does not look like a small horse's head. The snout does taper slightly and suggests the beginning of a muzzle, but at this stage the development is so slight that we should not notice it particularly if we did not know what was to come later. The brain was small and its structure was so primitive that it suggests the most primitive mammal brains, or even the brain of a reptile, more than it does that of the living horse or other modern ungulates.

All 44 teeth of the primitive mammalian dentition were still present in eohippus. In fact there has not been much tendency to reduce tooth number in horses, although the dentition has become extremely specialized in other respects. Even living horses sometimes have 44 teeth, but the usual number is 40 in the male and 36 in the female. In spite of retaining the full number of teeth, eohippus shows the beginning of the long gap, diastema, in each jaw between the incisors and the cheek teeth. The upper canine, a small tooth, occurs in the midst of this gap. The lower canine may be somewhat spaced, but is nearer the incisors and not sharply set off from them. The first premolars, upper and lower, tend to be spaced somewhat from the second premolars, a character lost in later horses in which the first premolars, when present, are vestigial teeth in contact with the large, functional second premolars. Altogether, eohippus shows a distinct but still incipient stage of the characteristic horse development of a double dental apparatus: a front set of teeth for nipping and picking up food and a separate back set for crushing and grinding food. The general shape of the mouth, especially the slender, flaring, somewhat spout-like front part of the lower jaw, suggests that the horse system of manipulating the food with the tongue was also under way in eohippus.

The premolars were still condylarth-like. The first and second were simple teeth with one or two outer but no inner cusps. The third and fourth premolars were somewhat more complicated, triangular in the upper jaw and with some development of inner cusps, but still sharply different from the molars and simpler than these. In the upper molars, the cusps seen in some condylarth teeth can be recognized, and no distinctly new cusps had been added, but the arrangement is somewhat different. The two outer cusps had a tendency, still slight, to form a united crest or wall. The front inner cusp and a smaller cusp near the midline of the tooth were beginning to form a crest, running inward and backward from the front outer corner of the tooth. A similar crest behind and parallel to this, not attached at its outer end, is beginning to form from the large back inner cusp and a smaller cusp near this on its outer side. In the lower teeth, too, the more separate and more conical cusps of the condylarth ancestry are beginning to lose their individuality as cusps and to form a crested or lophodont pattern.

All these dental characters, especially the differentiation of cropping and crushing apparatuses, reduction of canines, and tendency to form crests on the molars, show that in eohippus we have an animal that was becoming more particular about its food. It was already distinctly herbivorous. The teeth all had very low crowns and would not stand much wear by harsh herbage. The cheek teeth were beginning to grind as well as to crush, but the grinding function was still poorly developed. Such an animal certainly could not eat grass. (In fact, there probably was not much grass to eat at that time.) It must have lived mainly on succulent leaves with perhaps some of the softer seeds or small fruits to vary the diet. Eohippus was a primitive browser.

14

OTHER EOCENE HORSES

NOT long (geologically speaking) after eohippus spread over Europe and North America these two continents were separated. Migration between them stopped for the time being and animals evolved rather differently in the two regions. Eohippus had descendants in both, but they were distinct. Only the North American descendants gave rise to later horses and these are, of course, the most interesting for this history, but the European development also demands some notice. While in North America there was only one broad line of descent from eohippus through the Eocene and Oligocene, in Europe a number of divergent types arose and flourished throughout the Eocene.

One of these lines was relatively conservative. It is poorly known, mostly by teeth and jaw fragments, but these show that it remained very eohippus-like, with only some increase in size, loss of some of the less useful teeth, and moderate development of the grinding powers of the others. French paleontologists have given typical members of this group the jawbreaking names *Propachynolophus* (pro-pack-ee-noll'-o-fuss) and *Pachynolophus*. Even in the latest Eocene some of these die-hard primitive horses survived, but they then disappeared without issue. Other, better-known groups, such as the palaeotheres, were also derived from eohippus or something very like it, but became peculiarly specialized in various ways. They had some horse-like characters but were so distinctive that they are usually referred to a family of their own and not to the horse family. They will be mentioned again in a summary of horse relatives later in this book.

The more unified stock of North American Eocene horses was very conservative. It will become more and more apparent as the story is followed that horse evolution was not a simple matter of a line starting with eohippus and changing steadily until *Equus* was reached. The reality was somewhat more complex and yet much more understandable and natural in aspect than any such mysterious, steady, apparently purposeful progression would be. The rate of horse evolution, for one thing, varied greatly at different times and in different structures. In the Eocene the general rate was low and practically all the progress that was made was in the teeth.

There was no apparent tendency for increase in size in these Eocene horses. In fact some of the earliest species of eohippus, such as *Hyracotherium resartum* from the oldest Eocene beds of Wyoming, were larger than any known late Eocene horses. There were species of various sizes in all Eocene stages, but on the whole the smaller species seem to have been most successful then, and no general evolutionary size increase occurred. The limbs and body build were also nearly static, with no clear or pronounced evolutionary advance. The forefeet retained four toes and the hindfeet three toes, but the tiny vestiges of two more toes on the hindfeet (first and fifth) were lost.

There were more definite changes in the teeth, and in them several progressive stages can be observed. (See Fig. 14) The change was essentially continuous, and there was a good deal of variation at all times. Division of these horses into successive genera is therefore somewhat arbitrary, but it is convenient and customary to give separate generic names to the early Eocene horses, *Hyracotherium,* the middle Eocene horses, *Orohippus* (o'-roe-hip'-us) (see Plate XXIa), and the late Eocene horses, *Epihippus* (ep'-ee-hip'-us).

Hyracotherium is the technical name of eohippus and it has already been described. It was noted that all the premolars were unlike the molars in this stage and that the crests on the cheek teeth were not well developed. In *Orohippus* the last (fourth) premolar was almost like a molar in form and pattern and the crests were slightly more advanced, the cusps that enter into their formation being less distinctly separate. In *Epihippus* the last two premolars (third and fourth) were both almost exactly like molars (molariform), but the first two were still quite different. The crests were well formed. The outer crest (ectoloph) of the upper molars was sharp and continuous and had the form of two united crescents, like a somewhat flattened letter w. With some changes in details and proportions, this feature was inherited and retained in all the later horses.

Epihippus

14. Left upper cheek teeth of the three genera of North American Eocene fossil horses. Drawn to scale.

Orohippus

Eohippus

All Eocene horses retained low-crowned teeth, and their progressive evolution was almost entirely in molarization, the development of premolars with molar-like patterns, and in lophiodonty, the development of crested or ridged cheek teeth. (Fig. 14) Both of these changes are toward more strictly herbivorous dentitions and more effective teeth for browsing.

It happens that fossil mammals from around the very end of the Eocene and very beginning of the Oligocene have not been well known in North America. In recent years this gap in knowledge is being filled, but we still do not know enough about the animals of that important time of transition from one epoch to another. This applies also to the horses, and around this time there is a slight break in our otherwise practically continuous knowledge of horse history.

Occurring in the gap and helping to close it is a form usually considered a progressive subgenus of *Epihippus* and called *Epihippus* (*Duchesnehippus*) (*doo-shane'-hip-us*). (The name of a subgenus is written in parentheses after the name of the genus to which it belongs.) As its name indicates, it is from the Duchesne River beds of northeastern Utah, considered by some students to be of earliest Oligocene age and by others (including me) of latest Eocene. The teeth of this horse were more progressive than those of any typically Eocene form and more primitive than any of unquestioned Oligocene age, but somewhat nearer the earlier types. The skeleton is practically unknown and we can only guess that, when discovered, it may more fully confirm the reasonable inference that American Oligocene horses were directly derived from *Epihippus*. It remains possible, however, that the immediate ancestor of the Oligocene horses lived in some other region where its bones have not been found, and this was the opinion of the late W. D. Matthew, whose opinions are still entitled to the greatest respect. Even if this should prove to be true, however, we can be reasonably sure that the ancestor of the Oligocene horses was closely similar to *Epihippus*.

15

EARLY THREE-TOED HORSES

THE earliest horses definitely known to have had only three toes on the front feet belong to the genus *Mesohippus* (mezz'-o-hip'-us). (See Plate XXIIa, b) Horses of this group are very abundant in the picturesque, fossil-rich Big Badlands of South Dakota, in rocks of early and middle Oligocene age, and also occur in rocks of similar age elsewhere in western North America. This is one of the best known of all fossil horses because not only is it common, but also frequently it was buried and preserved without much scattering of the remains of the individual animals. In striking contrast with eohippus, for example, it is relatively easy to find a skeleton complete enough for reconstruction and mounting. There are at least 14 mounted skeletons of *Mesohippus* in American museums, many more than of any other kind of Tertiary horse.

Unlike the Eocene members of the horse family, *Mesohippus* must have looked a good deal like a small horse, so much so that if we could see one alive we might exclaim, 'Look at the tiny horse!'—and see the differences only when we looked more closely. Yet there were differences in every part of the body, and it took tens of millions of years of evolution to transform one line of *Mesohippus'* descendants into *Equus*.

The smallest species of *Mesohippus* were hardly larger than a large eohippus, but on the whole these Oligocene horses averaged considerably larger than Eocene horses. The typical height was probably about 6 hands (24 inches), although species considerably smaller and larger are known. There seems also to have been a real tendency for the average size to increase slowly during the Oligocene.

The head of *Mesohippus* was horsy and a typically equine muzzle was probably present, but the face as a whole was slender and the jaws were much shallower than in recent horses. The eye was set farther back than in Eocene horses, but still farther forward than in the living horse. The orbit was still open. The brain case had become swollen, and its internal cast shows a remarkable transformation in comparison with Eocene forms. The cerebral hemispheres, which are functionally associated with what we recognize as intelligence in animals (and in men, for that matter), had become much larger relatively and their surfaces had been thrown into a series of folds and grooves. The brain had become generally similar in type to a modern ungulate brain. The rather rapid rise of characteristic equine intelligence took place not with the origin of the family and appearance of eohippus, but during the transition from Eocene to Oligocene horses.

The neck of *Mesohippus* was relatively slightly shorter and less flexible than in most later horses, but the trunk was long and slender, the back somewhat more arched behind and less rigid than it was to become. The legs were long and slender, with the parts below the elbow and knee particularly elongate—adaptations for rapid running which in *Mesohippus* were already almost as well developed as in any later horse. The feet, however, all had three fully functional toes with a pad between and behind them. The middle toe was largest, as in Eocene horses, and the two side toes were little if any smaller than in the Eocene. The outer toe of the front foot, presence of which made all the Eocene horses four-toed, had disappeared, however, as far as any use or outer evidence was concerned and was represented only by a vestige, a small bony nodule attached to the wrist.

The teeth of *Mesohippus* were still low-crowned and fitted for browsing not grazing, but they had carried to practical completion the two progressive tendencies noted in the teeth of Eocene horses. Three premolars, the second to fourth, were now like the molars in pattern, and the set of crushing and grinding cheek teeth was a battery of six teeth all very nearly alike. This sort of evolutionary change was now complete and remained the same in all later horses.

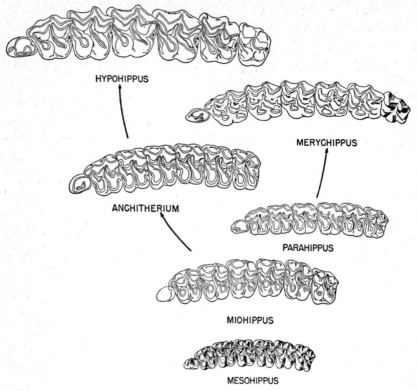

15. Left upper cheek teeth of some genera of Oligocene and Miocene North American fossil horses. Drawn to scale.

Three premolars and the three molars thereafter evolved together without becoming either more or less similar. The first premolar never did tend to become complex or molar-like but remained small and simple and eventually tended to be eliminated. The crests that had been developing on the cheek teeth throughout the Eocene were fully formed, sharp, and continuous in *Mesohippus,* but no new crests or spurs, such as were to be important in later horse evolution, had yet appeared. (See Fig. 15)

It is interesting that the upper incisors of *Mesohippus* show the first trace of the 'mark' or pit so characteristic of most later horses. In this genus, it was barely beginning to develop and did not yet occur on the lower incisors.

The more progressive horses of the middle Oligocene and all the horses of the late Oligocene are placed by convention in a separate genus, *Miohippus* (my'-o-hip'-us). (Plate XXIb) In fact *Mesohippus* and *Miohippus* intergrade so perfectly and the differences between them are so slight and variable that even experts find it difficult, at times nearly impossible, to distinguish them clearly. In general the species of *Miohippus* are larger. On the upper cheek teeth, the outer end of the oblique posterior crest (metaloph) sometimes has a small branch or spur (the crochet) that projects forward. This apparently insignificant addition became a constant and characteristic feature in many later horses, but was merely an occasional variation in *Miohippus*. Another small but important feature first appears in the hind foot of *Miohippus* and has been used to distinguish that genus from *Mesohippus*. In earlier horses the long cannon bone (metatarsal) of the third or middle toe comes in contact with only a single one of the ankle bones (the ectocuneiform). In *Miohippus* and all later horses this joint is broader and stronger, and the cannon bone also comes into contact with the outer ankle bone (the cuboid).

After *Miohippus* the history of the horse became considerably more complicated. It is no longer a matter of following what appears to be a single great lineage as in the American *Hyracotherium* → *Orohippus* → *Epihippus* → *Mesohippus* → *Miohippus* sequence. Now the horses tend once more to split up into various different groups which evolved separately and in somewhat different ways. (Something of the sort had happened earlier in the Old World, but not in America, among the descendants of eohippus.) *Miohippus* lived on into the earliest Miocene and there it intergraded with several different descendant groups. (See Fig. 15) It is sad that this introduces possible confusion into the story, but there is not much point in criticizing nature for something that happened some millions of years ago. It would also be foolish to try to ignore the complications, which did occur and which are a very important part of the record. Most accounts of horse evolution have simplified the situation to the point of definitely falsifying it. Let us here face the facts of the record and try to follow them as clearly as possible but without misleading omissions.

The most conservative, or least rapidly evolving, of lines derived from *Miohippus* are characterized by the facts that they retained relatively low-crowned teeth, continuing throughout their history to be browsing and not grazing animals, and that they also retained three toes on each foot without noteworthy further reduction of the side toes. It has been supposed that these animals were especially addicted to life in woods and forests, where they ate the leaves of trees and bushes and where the three-toed feet may have given them firmer footing in the soft soil. These living conditions are also found along river banks and that may have been their preferred habitat instead of, or along with, forests.

One of these groups, beginning with the genus *Anchitherium* (ank'-ee-thee'-ree-um), included great travelers. In these horses the teeth remained very simple. (Fig. 15) The upper cheek teeth did not even have the slight complication of the extra spur (crochet) that sometimes occurred as a variation in *Miohippus,* and their only real advance was that the hinder oblique crest (metaloph) became firmly attached to the outer crest (ectoloph), from which it had been separated by a small cleft in *Miohippus* and all earlier horses. The lower cheek teeth were also simple, with a plain W-pattern.

Anchitherium apparently arose from *Miohippus* early in the Miocene and in North America. (In some works on the evolution of the horse, these early American anchitheres are called *Kalobatippus* [cal-o-bat'-ip-us], but they are so like typical *Anchitherium* that I use that name for them.) These animals soon migrated to the Old World, and they flourished all over Europe and Asia during most of the Miocene.

The various descendants of eohippus had died out in the Old World by early Oligocene times, and no horse remains have been found in Oligocene deposits there. It is not really clear why this should be. Other animals migrated between North America and Eurasia in the early Oligocene and horses (*Mesohippus*) were common enough in North America then, but for some reason *Mesohippus* did not make the grand tour as far as we know. Later in the Oligocene the continents were probably separated by sea again, so that horses could not wander from one to the other, but a dry land route arose around the end of the Oligocene and was utilized by *Anchitherium* as soon as that genus arose. Anchitheres became rather varied in Eurasia and there is some suggestion that they split up into two or more new lines of descent there, but the details have not been surely established as yet.

The anchitheres that remained in America continued to evolve and gave rise here to *Hypohippus* (high'-po-hip'-us). (Plate XXIIIa, b and Fig. 15) These horses were very like *Anchitherium,* but they were larger and they developed to greater degree a pocket in the bones on the side of the face. (The possible meaning of this peculiar feature will be discussed briefly in connection with *Pliohippus* in which it also occurs.) *Hypohippus* probably also migrated to Eurasia at a later date and has been recorded in the Pliocene of China. Unfortunately the European and Asiatic specimens of *Anchitherium* and *Hypohippus* so far described are so incomplete that we cannot be absolutely sure of their relationships. It is possible, although at this writing it seems unlikely, that the Chinese *Hypohippus* was the last survivor of some line of Old World anchitheres and not an immigrant.

In America there is another offshoot of the *Hypohippus* group that is very poorly known but distinctive enough to have been given a separate name: *Megahippus* (meg'-ah-hip'-us). It was unusually large for its time (early Pliocene, the same age as our last true *Hypohippus*) and had strange, enlarged, spoon-like incisors in the lower jaw pointing more forward than upward.

The anchitheres in general, *Anchitherium, Hypohippus, Megahippus,* and perhaps some other forms now too poorly known to merit special discussion, can hardly be dismissed as a mere side-line in horse evolution. It is true that they were outside the ancestry of our living horses and that they died out long ago, in the Pliocene. They represent, however, the logical outcome of the sort of horse evolution that was going on through the Eocene and the Oligocene. As nearly as there is a straight line of horse evolution, it culminated and ended with these animals, which, like their ancestors, were multiple-toed browsers. From this point of view, it is the line leading to modern horses that was the side branch, even though it outlasted the straighter line of horse evolution. (See Fig. 13)

One other peculiar and extinct group should be mentioned before turning back to the ancestry of the modern horse: the pigmy horses of the Miocene. These are united under the name *Archaeohippus* (ark'-ee-o-hip'-us). They are not very well known, and it is possible that more than one group derived from *Miohippus* or earliest *Parahippus* (see below) became dwarfed and is included under this one name. In any case they are all much alike and resemble miniature *Miohippus*. They were generally much smaller than other Miocene horses, about the size of a small *Mesohippus,* some of them perhaps no larger than some eohippuses. These little horses must have been remarkably graceful and attractive. It is a pity that the skeleton is so incompletely known that no mounted specimen or restoration can yet be made. At any rate this reversal of the usual, but by no means constant, tendency for the horses to increase in size is of extraordinary interest. We shall see also that other, quite different, groups of pigmy horses evolved at a later date, in the Pliocene.

16

THE GREAT TRANSFORMATION

WHILE the anchitheres and archaeohips were continuing what might be called the old school of horse evolution, another, more abundant, and ultimately more successful group in North America was striking out along a new line. These horses were learning to eat grass and acquiring the sort of teeth (and digestive systems, but these can only be inferred in the fossils) that enabled them to do so. They were changing over from browsing animals to grazing animals, still herbivores but with a profound change in their way of life. It is not likely to be a coincidence that at the same time grass became common, as judged by fossil grass seeds in the rocks. A rich food supply was becoming increasingly abundant, and it was one not available to most of the herbivores then living. The horses exploited it and this was surely a crucial factor in their abundance in the later Tertiary and their survival to our times.

Grass is a harsh food. The blades and seeds contain abrasive silica, and grass cropped near the ground is also bound to contain dust and grit. The earlier horses and the anchitheres could not live on grass, even if it were available, because it would have worn out their low, simply ridged teeth while they were still young. On such a diet, too few of them would have survived long enough to breed and to maintain the race. A successful grazing animal needs high teeth with complex, deep ridges that will wear and keep a good grinding surface for a long time. Teeth like this were acquired during the Miocene by horses of the successive genera *Parahippus* (pair'-ah-hip'-us) and *Merychippus* (mare'-ee-kip'-us).

Parahippus arose in the early Miocene from *Miohippus* and its earlier species were, of course, very like that ancestor. The transition is marked by the general establishment of characters that were already appearing in *Miohippus* as occasional variations. At first the only really clear distinction was in such minor, but useful and promising, characters as the constant presence on the upper cheek teeth of the little, new, spur-like crest called a crochet by students of the family, and the firm and constant connection of the oblique posterior crest, called the metaloph, with the outer crest, the ectoloph. In more progressive forms the crochet became stronger and met and united with the middle of the oblique anterior crest, the protoloph. At the same time a small median posterior cusp, the hypostyle, which had been present but variable and of no particular importance in earlier forms, grew up and formed a transverse connection between the metaloph and the ectoloph along the posterior margin of the tooth.

These changes may sound somewhat intricate if the terms are unfamiliar, but the modification of form was rather simple as can be seen by examination of Fig. 15. The change was, however, profoundly important and worked a real transformation of the pattern of the tooth and radical increase in its grinding power. The old browsing tooth pattern of an outer crest, W-shaped since *Epihippus*, with two oblique crests running inward from it is no longer apparent. Its elements are still there, but the new small crests and connections, with changes in direction and proportions of some of the ridges, have produced a pattern more like two W's, one outer and one inner, with cross connections along the front, middle, and back of the tooth. Between them are two valleys or pits, the prefossette and the postfossette, entirely enclosed by crests. In addition to this double-W pattern, the two original inner cusps of eohippus persist as prominent pillars. The more anterior of these, the protocone, is sometimes separate and sometimes attached to the anterior crescent of the inner W, while the more posterior, the hypocone, is always attached to the posterior crescent. In the lower cheek teeth the rather simple single-W pattern of the browsers became modified and complicated at the same time by the growth of crests and pillars along the open inner side of the W.

The net result of all these modifications was a cheek dentition that was increasingly and in the end excellently adapted for grinding by motion of the lower jaws from side to side against the upper jaws—the chewing action familiar to everyone in our modern horse. The resistance and efficiency of the incisors was also increased at this time by the completion of the pit or mark in the upper incisors and its appearance in the lower incisors.

These tooth pattern changes developed with much variation and fluctuation but in a generally progressive way in *Parahippus* and continued in its middle and upper Miocene descendant *Merychippus*. As usual when we have a good fossil record from the region which was the center of evolution of such a group, the transition from one genus to the next was gradual and the line drawn between them from purposes of classification is arbitrary. In the later species of *Merychippus* the tooth pattern was fully established, practically as in all later horses, and its evolution after the Miocene involved only relatively insignificant variation and modification of details.

While this pattern was being developed in *Parahippus* and *Merychippus,* two other important tooth changes, also necessary for the change over from browsing to grazing, were likewise occurring. One of these was an increase in the height of the crowns of the teeth. (See Fig. 16) In browsing horses the crown was low. When the tooth had moved into position, the whole crown protruded from the gums and the tooth remained stable, anchored to the roots in their sockets and ending at the gum line—the same arrangement as in our own teeth, a condition called brachydonty ('short-toothedness'). With the increase in crown height in *Parahippus* and *Merychippus,* only the end of the crown protruded from the gum when the tooth first came into use and started grinding. The rest of the crown was still buried in a large bony socket as a reserve for future use. As wear removed tooth material from the grinding surface, the whole tooth kept moving out so that a good grinding surface was maintained continuously until the whole crown was gone and the roots finally reached the gum line—if, as was not usually the case, the animal lived so long. This system is called hypsodonty ('long-toothedness').

The other important tooth change at this time was the development
of an entirely new substance in the teeth. In low-crowned teeth, like
those of the browsing horses and of man, there are as a rule two
resistant materials: a hard, glistening layer of enamel, which caps the
whole crown, and a softer but still solid, ivory-like material called
dentine, which occurs under the enamel and is exposed only when this

16. Vertical sections
through upper molar
teeth of an early brows-
ing horse (*Miohippus*,
left), with low-crowned
teeth, and of one of its
descendants, an early
grazing horse (*Merychip-
pus*, right), with high-
crowned teeth. Note the
great heightening of the
enamel ridges and the
filling in of pockets with
cement. Drawn to scale.

MIOHIPPUS   MERYCHIPPUS

⌒ *ENAMEL*   〰 *DENTINE*

▒ *CEMENT*   P *PULP CAVITY*

is worn through. In high-crowned teeth, as the crests wear down each
has a projecting enamel rim and a central channel, somewhat
hollowed out because the material is softer, on the dentine. If the
grooves and pockets between the crests remained empty as the crown
became higher and they became deeper, they would become a
serious weakness. The enamel ridges, supported on one side only
(the dentine side), would easily break and splinter. The deep pockets
would also tend to fill up with decaying bits of food. This difficulty
was avoided in the horses (and in most other high-crowned, grazing
animals) by the deposition of cement, a bone-like substance somewhat like dentine but slightly softer, outside the enamel. This came
to form a protective cap all around the crown and to fill completely
the deep valleys and pockets of the grinding surface. Cement was

absent in the more primitive species of *Parahippus* but began to
appear as a thin film in the more progressive forms. In *Merychippus*
it was always present and finally reached full development.

The transformation of the dentition from browsing to grazing
type was the most radical change that ever occurred in the evolution
of horse teeth. It occurred in one main group only of the several
that then existed in the horse family, and it took place entirely within the Miocene epoch. Tooth evolution in that particular group
and during that limited time was much more rapid than in any
other line of horses or than at any time before or since the Miocene.

Evolution in other parts of the body in *Parahippus* and *Merychippus* was considerably less rapid than in the teeth, but changes
were occurring. For the most part these continued tendencies already
visible in the earlier browsing horses. There was some increase in
size and some species of *Merychippus* reached a height of at least
10 hands (40 inches)—as large as many living ponies. (See Plate
XXIVa, b) The skull was becoming very *Equus*-like. The muzzle
elongated relative to the cranium, and the eye was set almost as far
back in the head as in recent horses. The orbit became closed by a
bony bar behind. The jaws deepened markedly, as was necessary
to hold the lengthening tooth crowns. The body and leg proportions
differed considerably in various species. Some were rather strong
and stocky, others slender and fleet, but on the whole the proportions were not strikingly different from those of living horses.

In the forearm and shin there were changes that had long been
under way and now culminated. In primitive mammals—including
man, a primitive mammal in this respect—there are two separate
bones, radius and ulna, in the forearm, and likewise two, tibia and
fibula, in the shin. These are both movable and they permit rather
free rotation of the forefeet (or hands) and hindfeet. In Eocene
and Oligocene horses this rotation was becoming sharply limited,
but the radius and ulna and the tibia and fibula remained complete
and separate, although the ulna and the fibula were becoming relatively more slender and less movable. In *Merychippus* adults, the
ulna had fused solidly with the radius and was no longer movable
as a separate unit, while the fibula had lost much of its shaft and

been reduced to a practically functionless spike of bone projecting downward from the head of the tibia. These conditions were retained in all later horses with little change except for still more reduction of the now useless shaft of the ulna. The projecting upper end of the ulna, corresponding with our funny-bone, continued to be essential as a muscle attachment and was not reduced, but it functioned as if it were part of the radius, with which it was firmly united.

These changes eliminated practically all rotating motion of the feet. Along with other specializations in the joints of the legs, they are related to the fact that horses use their limbs only for locomotion (or kicking) and not for holding, manipulation, and the like as do men, cats, squirrels, and many other animals that retain more flexible limbs. Horses also walk or run in a peculiarly limited and specialized, although highly effective, way. Within the leg, the joints work only in a fore-and-aft plane and it is practically impossible to rotate the leg or to bend part of it outward or inward. The leg is a rigid machine for carrying weight and for moving forward. What side motion is possible (and some is necessary so that the legs can pass in galloping, for instance) comes from the shoulder and hip joints.

The feet of *Parahippus* and *Merychippus* retained three toes. The side toes were still complete, visible externally, and ended in small hooves. In some of the less progressive species the side toes were still fairly large, but in advanced forms they were short and small. In such forms the primitive foot-pad of their ancestors had been lost. The weight was carried by the big central toe, which ended in a large, convex hoof very like that of *Equus* and which was carried by a likewise *Equus*-like cannon bone.

All in all, a progressive *Merychippus* was very near our recent horses in general structure. If we saw one alive, we should probably take it for an ordinary pony, unless we happened to notice that it had small extra toes or 'dew hooves' and unless it had zebra-like stripes or some other peculiar color pattern—a possibility that cannot be checked from the fossil remains.

17

LATER THREE-TOED HORSES

MERYCHIPPUS, the horse with the new look, was a sensational
success. It is abundant in all the middle and late Miocene
mammal faunas of North America and it soon included a great
number of varieties and species. In later Miocene times several
rather distinctive groups are recognizable. In one, more typical of
Merychippus, the front inner cusp, the protocone, of the upper cheek
teeth formed a separate pillar and was not united to the rest of the
enamel ridge pattern until near the base of the tooth. In another
group this union occurred high on the crown and the protocone
appears united to the rest of the pattern after the earliest wear
stages. This group has been given a separate name, *Protohippus*
(pro'-toe-hip'-us), which figures in most discussions of the evolution
of the horse. The difference is really very slight, however, and most
students now prefer to call all these horses *Merychippus,* with
Merychippus (Protohippus) as a subgenus.

Slight and unimportant as this one tooth character was, in itself,
it is a handy way to recognize the beginning of another important
event in horse history. By the end of the Miocene, the grazing horses
had split into at least six fairly distinct lines. (See Figs. 13 and 17)
Most of these retained three toes and they represent, with minor differences in the various groups, the continuation and completion of
the sort of evolution that began in *Parahippus* and went forward so
actively in *Merychippus.* It happens that later three-toed forms arose
from ancestors with the more typical late *Merychippus* character of
having the protocone attachment nearer the base of the crown. Other
lines arose from the *Merychippus (Protohippus)* type with more ex-

tended protocone attachment. Among these, one quickly became one-toed and it led eventually to *Equus*, as will be discussed in the next section.

This splitting up of the advanced grazing horses was the same sort of evolutionary event, on a still larger scale, as the splitting of the advanced browsing horses in the early Miocene. The browsing horses had now nearly run their course and were no longer numerous. *Hypohippus* and its poorly known, larger, close relative *Megahippus* still occurred in America, and *Anchitherium* in the Old World, but they were all to die out during the Pliocene.

Among the three-toed grazers, a conservative line, inseparable from *Merychippus*, persisted in the early Pliocene and then became extinct. More durable and important were the three closely similar and related groups *Hipparion* (hip-pair'-ee-on), *Neohipparion* (nee'-oh-), and *Nannippus* (nan-nip'-pus). (See Fig. 17) All of them differ from *Merychippus* in having the grinding teeth with higher crowns. This character is here carried to its efficient extreme. The difference from *Merychippus* is clear-cut and, indeed, obvious when the most characteristic forms are compared, but the change was gradual and even an expert is puzzled as to where to draw the line in the continuous series from advanced *Merychippus* to primitive *Hipparion*, *Neohipparion*, or *Nannippus*. The differences between these three genera are also so slight and variable as sometimes to puzzle the experts and, indeed, they are unimportant to anyone but an expert except as they do serve to show the diversity of horses of this general sort. The following brief notes will usually, but not always, permit distinction of these genera by their upper cheek teeth:

In *Hipparion* these teeth are usually rather straight and have the separate inner column, the protocone, round or oval. The enamel pattern has numerous small folds and these may become more complicated than in the related forms. *Neohipparion* and *Nannippus* both have the teeth curved inward. In *Neohipparion* the protocone is usually long in the fore-and-aft direction and flattened from side to side. In *Nannippus* the protocones may be like those of some *Hipparion* or those of some *Neohipparion*, but they are often intermediate, neither short and oval nor long and flattened but roughly twice as long as wide and lens-shaped on the grinding surface. *Nannippus* teeth are smaller than those of the other two groups and in the latest *Nannippus* they reached an extreme length and slenderness not equaled by any other horses.

All these horses retained complete side-toes as in *Merychippus*.

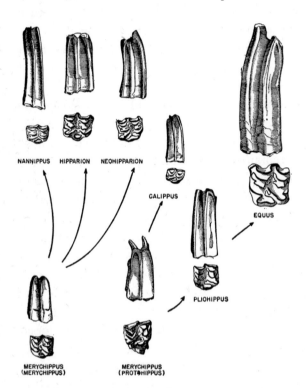

NANNIPPUS   HIPPARION   NEOHIPPARION

CALIPPUS

EQUUS

PLIOHIPPUS

MERYCHIPPUS
(MERYCHIPPUS)

MERYCHIPPUS
(PROTOHIPPUS)

17. Upper molar teeth of some of the principal genera of grazing (high-crowned) horses in the Miocene and Pliocene. For each genus, both the grinding surface (below) and the outer face (above) are shown for a single molar removed from the jaw. Drawn to scale.

These were variable but as a rule they were relatively as large as in *Merychippus* and in some cases they may even have increased in size. They probably did not quite touch the ground when the animals stood on firm, level ground, but they may still have had some usefulness. Differences in size and build were, of course, strong among the various species. A characteristic *Neohipparion* was a rather slender but well set up animal, suggestive of a light cowpony both in size and in proportions. (See Plate XXVa, b) Some forms of *Hipparion* were heavier, stockier animals. *Nannippus* was a pigmy, one of the relatively uncommon groups of animals (like *Archaeohippus*, mentioned on a previous page) that tended to become smaller rather than larger as it evolved. Some of the late specimens were miniatures no higher than a small Shetland pony and considerably more slender. These graceful creatures had long, thin legs and feet, and the general form probably suggested a small gazelle more than an ordinary horse. (The legs and various parts of the skeleton are fairly well known in some species, such as *Nannippus phlegon* from the Panhandle of Texas, but unfortunately no skeleton has yet been mounted.)

Hipparion was one of the great animal travelers. When it originated, a dry-land route from the New to the Old World existed by way of Alaska and Siberia. *Hipparion* crossed by this route almost immediately after it originated, and these horses flourished all over Asia and Europe. Their remains occur in Pliocene strata, sometimes in great heaps, at innumerable localities from China to western Europe, including India, central Asia, Greece, Spain, and many other places. Horses of this lineage also entered Africa, and remains of their descendants have been found far down toward the Cape. As far as we know, they were the first horses to enter Africa. Fossil mammals are, however, poorly known in that continent, and it seems likely that the anchitheres, so widespread in Eurasia during the Miocene, also reached parts, at least, of Africa.

In Africa during the Pliocene a branch of *Hipparion* developed and became so distinct that it is often considered a separate genus, *Stylohipparion* (sty'-lo-hip-pair'-ee-on). The enamel folds of its teeth were unusually complicated, and the lower cheek teeth frequently had an extra pillar that occurs in other horses only as a relatively rare variation. These animals survived into the Pleistocene in Africa and lived there along with the immediate ancestors of the zebras. They became extinct before the Recent, but as far as now known they were the last three-toed horses in the world.

Neohipparion and *Nannippus* were exclusively North American, as far as known. *Neohipparion* became extinct before the end of the Pliocene. *Nannippus* was the last American three-toed horse and was still rather common in the transitional time from Pliocene to Pleistocene.

One other line of Pliocene three-toed horses, although they have no great importance for our story, may be mentioned briefly, merely for the sake of completeness. This is the genus *Calippus* (cal-ip'-us), derived from the protocone-united group *Merychippus* (*Protohippus*) and with teeth nearly like those of *Pliohippus* (see below). These were small horses and might be called another line of pigmies. They were uncommon, lived only from latest Miocene through the early Pliocene, and are not well known.

18

ONE-TOED HORSES

FROM our point of view, the most important of the groups
that arose from *Merychippus* in the latest Miocene was *Pliohippus* (ply'-o-hip'-us). (Plate XXVIa, b) It was in this genus, and apparently in this genus alone among the eight or more that occur
in the early Pliocene, that the side-toes were finally lost. This one-
toed condition was, of course, retained in the various descendants of
Pliohippus, including *Equus.*

The origin of the one-toed from a three-toed horse must surely be
taken as one of the landmarks in horse history, and yet by the time
it occurred the really final step was neither striking nor particularly
important. The side toes had then been reduced to the point of
having no special significance or use, and their further reduction,
so that they were no longer visible from the outside in a living animal, was a slight change. It is, in fact, somewhat difficult to be sure
whether the change had yet occurred in a given case. Perfectly preserved feet of *Pliohippus* are rare and the tiny bones of the reduced
side toes are readily lost. Some of the most primitive forms of *Pliohippus* did still have minute side toes with tiny joints still projecting, and some of the more advanced forms had evidently lost
these. There was probably much variation in this respect, and even
in a single group of *Pliohippus* some may have had the toes and some
not. It cannot have made much if any difference in the efficiency of
the animal, and in such cases wide variation is usual. When the
toes disappeared as such, vestiges of them remained as long splint
bones underneath the skin on each side of the cannon bone.

The teeth in *Pliohippus* increased in height still more than in

Merychippus and much as in the contemporary Pliocene three-toed horses (See Fig. 17) The pattern was closely similar to that in *Neohipparion* except for rather insignificant details, but they are distinguishable at a glance by the fact that the protocone was almost always attached in *Pliohippus* even in early wear stages. The pattern was almost precisely like that of the simpler variants among later and modern *Equus*. There are some differences, of course, but they are so slight and variable that it is not worth while to go into detail about them in this general account. There was some tendency to complicate the grinding surface by addition of small extra folds in later horses and this probably did increase efficiency to a moderate extent. Other details help to distinguish various species and groups of species but seem to have no particular biological importance.

There is one difference, not in the pattern but in the over-all shape of the upper cheek teeth, that usually permits easy distinction between *Pliohippus* and *Equus* teeth. When these teeth began to elongate considerably in *Merychippus*, growth was more rapid on the outer side than on the inner. The result was that the complete tooth crown was curved, convex on the outer side and concave on the inner. As had been noted, this was still true in varying degree in *Neohipparion* and *Nannippus*. It was particularly strong in *Pliohippus*, descendent of *Merychippus* in a different line. In *Equus*, growth had become more equalized and its teeth were and are almost straight. (The front and back teeth are curved forward or backward for better fit into the jaw, but this is quite a different matter from the sideward curving in *Merychippus* and *Pliohippus*.) (See Fig. 18)

The skull of *Pliohippus* had one puzzling peculiarity not found in *Equus*. The bones of the side of the face, in front of the eye, were usually hollowed out to varying degree so that the skull here has a more or less deep pocket. (Fig. 19) In extreme form, this is rather complex with three main extensions, one upward immediately in front of the eye, one on the face below and in front of this, and one backward into the base of the cheek bone. Similar pockets had appeared on the skull in some other groups of horses, such as *Hypohippus* and *Archaeohippus*. The meaning of this peculiarity has been heatedly discussed and is really a mystery. It does not seem to

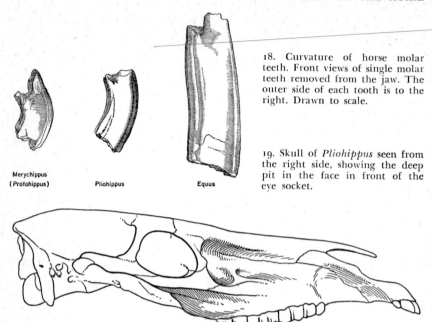

18. Curvature of horse molar teeth. Front views of single molar teeth removed from the jaw. The outer side of each tooth is to the right. Drawn to scale.

Merychippus
(Protohippus)   Pliohippus   Equus

19. Skull of *Pliohippus* seen from the right side, showing the deep pit in the face in front of the eye socket.

have been of any great value or importance, because it is highly variable when it does occur, it may be present in one horse and absent in another even though the two are closely related, and it has been lost in *Equus,* which, by the test of survival, is the most advanced and efficient of all horses. Yet it must have had some meaning or it would not have appeared so often in various different sorts of horses. Some authorities think the pocket was occupied by a gland. Others suppose it was developed to lodge muscles to move an unusually flexible nose. Still others maintain that it was a means of strengthening the skull as this became larger and deeper and before this region was fully remodeled to lodge the sockets of the enlarged cheek teeth. What was probably the most careful study yet made (by W. K. Gregory) came to the conclusion that in these horses the small fleshy sack found just inside the nostrils in *Equus* was much larger and extended back into the bony hollow or pits. No one knows for sure, and this is a good example of how exceedingly difficult it may be to interpret structures in fossils when they differ radically from anything known in living animals.

The more advanced species of *Pliohippus* were so like modern horses that further evolution was a matter of refinement of details rather than of any essential change. *Equus,* in a broad sense, arose at the end of the Pliocene from the subgenus *Pliohippus (Astrohippus)* (as'-tro-hip'-us). There was slight final lengthening of the cheek teeth, and they became straighter and in most species, somewhat more complicated in minor variable details.

The earliest species of *Equus* in North America have simpler teeth than most of the later forms and are different in a few minor details, some primitive and some perhaps not. They have been placed in a separate subgenus *Equus (Plesippus)* (please-ip'-us). (Plate XXVIIa, b) Similar horses also appear in the earliest Pleistocene of Europe, for example, *Equus stenonis* of Italy. *Equus* migrated to the Old World soon after it arose in North America and while still in this more primitive stage.

It used to be maintained, and still is by many if not by most students, that the most advanced horses, *the* horses in the strictest sense, *Equus (Equus)*, also arose in America as a development from *Equus (Plesippus)*, and also migrated from here to the Old World. The history must, however, have been somewhat more complicated than this would suggest, and in fact the details are not really established. In spite of the very abundant fossil material available and the interest of this final stage of horse evolution, an adequate and conclusive study has yet to be made. *Equus (Plesippus)* was quite zebralike in some respects. One student (P. O. McGrew) insists that it was a zebra and should be considered the same as the zebra subgenus, *Equus (Hippotigris)* (hip'-o-tie'-griss). He supposes that the zebras only arose in North America, migrated to Africa through Eurasia, and then became extinct except in Africa. In the meantime, he thinks, *Equus (Equus)* arose in Asia from a distinctly different line of *Pliohippus* (which is, however, wholly unknown in Eurasia) and then migrated from Asia to North America, not in the opposite direction. There is nothing unreasonable in this theory and it may prove to be true, but it is not sufficiently supported at present. There are several alternative possibilities that still appear more probable to some students. An ancestry for *Equus (Equus)* is not known in

Eurasia unless it be *Equus* (*Plesippus*), which was also North American. Horse evolution had been centered in North America since early Eocene, and all migration had been from here to Europe. The evidence so far advanced that *Equus* (*Plesippus*) is the same as *Equus* (*Hippotigris*) is not fully convincing. Even if this is correct, *Equus* (*Equus*) may well have arisen from primitive zebras—even the living zebras are more primitive than the 'true' horses and could conceivably be ancestral types for them. On the other hand, *Equus* (*Plesippus*) may resemble the zebras simply because both are primitive types of *Equus*.

Dispute whether the final horse migration was from North America to Asia or from Asia to North America should not confuse the essential facts. It seems practically certain that *Equus* arose from *Pliohippus* and then spread rapidly almost all over the world. In the million years or more of its existence, *Equus* has migrated in numerous different directions and at many different times, and it has developed many distinct forms. The tangled threads of this fabric have not been fully unraveled. (Fig. 20)

Equus remains occur in Pleistocene deposits nearly everywhere. (Plate XXVIIIa, b) They are probably more widespread and abundant than any other single sort of fossil bones. They are found throughout Africa, Europe, and Asia, and here we have come around again to the beginning of the story of the recent horses. *Equus* missed Australia, because there was no land route to the island continent. In North America it occurs all the way from Alaska to Patagonia and may be found in every state in the union. Wild horses were still here when the first Indians arrived but were extinct in both the Americas before white men had reached here.

South America has now been mentioned for the first time in this history and we should now go back a bit to give some special notice of that continent. From the early Tertiary until some time in the Pliocene, South America was isolated from the rest of the world. When eohippus appeared in North America there was a strait instead of an isthmus between North and South America. Horses could not cross, and none reached South America until almost the end of horse history. The barrier was still there in the early Pliocene,

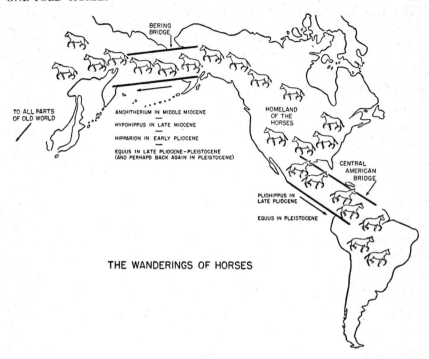

THE WANDERINGS OF HORSES

20. The wanderings of horses. The place of origin of the horse family is unknown. After the origin, North America was the homeland for the family and from here horses spread periodically to other parts of the world over two land bridges: the Bering Bridge (now flooded) and the Panama Bridge (still standing).

when *Neohipparion* and early *Pliohippus* spread well down into tropical central America. Later in the Pliocene the Isthmus of Panama arose and horses promptly took advantage of the new opportunity. Some advanced sort of *Pliohippus* wandered down into South America and there, with a whole new continent to exploit, its descendants soon became abundant and varied. (Fig. 20)

In South America, these late Pliocene horses evolved rather rapidly into three distinct types, all confined to that continent. *Hippidion* (Plate XXIXa, b), best known of these southern horses, was similar to a stocky, short-legged, one-toed *Pliohippus*. The nasal bones (the pair of long bones supporting the bridge of the nose) were even longer than in *Equus* but had no bony support except for the attachment at the extreme back end. In life the bone must have

been well supported by a nasal septum of cartilage and other tissues, but the lack of bony support gives these skulls a strange look
unlike any other known animal. The skull is also unusually slender,
compressed from side to side, in comparison with its great length
and depth. The eye was smaller than in most horses and was set
unusually low in the head.

Onohippidium (oh'-no-hip-pid'-ee-um), a second genus peculiar to
South America, had a similar skull but retained the large pits on the
face mentioned above as particularly characteristic of some species
of the ancestral form *Pliohippus*. The third genus of this group,
Parahipparion (pair'-a-hip-pair'-ee-on), was characterized by particularly short feet. (This animal is called *Hyperhippidium* in most
books, and that is a better name for a beast more closely allied to
Hippidion than to *Hipparion,* but *Parahipparion* was historically
the first name applied to it and must be retained.) W. B. Scott considered this short-footed form a mountain animal adapted for climb-
ing. On the other hand, *Hippidion* was also rather short-legged,
though less so, and it was apparently a common animal of the open
pampa.

In the Pleistocene there was a new invasion from North America,
and then modern horses of the *Equus* (*Equus*) type entered the
southern continent. They soon replaced the older immigrants
and ranged almost everywhere from tropical valleys along the
equator to the bleak shores of the Straits of Magellan. As in North
America, they survived the Ice Age and were still going strong in
early recent times and after the Indians were established in South
America, but then became mysteriously and completely extinct.
There are, indeed, persistent legends that wild horses still lived
in the Argentine when the Spaniards arrived there and that their
blood is mingled with that of jinetas in the feral pampas horses, but
careful study by A. Cabrera and others indicates that these legends
are—just legends.

The extinction of horses over the whole of North and South
America, where they had roamed in vast herds during the Pleistocene,
is one of the most mysterious episodes of animal history. There is
no doubt about the fact, but the reason for it is doubtful to say

the least. There has been no lack of speculation and a dozen possible explanations have been suggested, but all of these lack evidence and none is really satisfactory. Some possibilities can be rather definitely ruled out. It was not the glaciation of the great Ice Age of the Pleistocene that caused the extinction of horses. Many of them lived in regions not appreciably affected by the glaciers. Moreover the horses were abundant all during the glacial epoch, which they survived only to become extinct after the retreat of the last ice sheets was well under way.

The cause was not the disappearance of prairie grasses or suitable forage for horses. Other grazing animals, especially the bison, which had lived on similar forage and along with the horses through the Pleistocene, continued in undiminished numbers. It was not the competition of these other grazers that ended the horses, because horses became extinct in areas, such as all of South America, where there were no bison, and when reintroduced in historic times they thrived on plains also occupied by the bison herds. It was not an environmental change making the region as a whole unsuitable for horses: the continents were greatly varied and yet horses everywhere died out in the Americas. The very rapid spread of feral horses after the domestic horse was introduced in both North and South America shows that the plains areas were ideally suited for horses, and there is no reason to think that such environments were wholly lacking here when the horses became extinct. The cause was not a new enemy, some horseflesh-loving carnivore (other than man). No such enemy appeared and spread over the Americas during the extinction time of the horses. On the contrary, some probable enemies of theirs, such as the dire-wolves and the sabertooth cats, died out along with them.

These suggestions eliminated, few possible explanations remain. Were the horses all carried off by some plague, perhaps a fly-borne epidemic such as sleeping sickness or some other deadly and new infection? This is a possibility and a tempting one, but it cannot be checked. If the last horses all died from the same epidemic, no evidence is provided by their fossil remains. If such an epidemic occurred, how did the prong-horn antelopes, the bison, and other animals that lived along with the horses escape it? (Sleeping sickness, often suggested as the possible disease in question, is fatal to a great variety of animals in Africa and by no means confined to horses or to any one species or genus.) Thus there are objections, but disease cannot be ruled out as the possible cause, or as a contributing cause.

Did man possibly kill off the horses? It is now clear that wild horses still survived both in North and in South America when the earliest Indians reached these lands, perhaps ten thousand years ago. These Indians probably killed horses for food—but in North America they certainly killed large numbers of bison, and bison did not become extinct. If horses were already on the wane, the herds becoming few and weak, then persecution by man might have provided the finishing touch. It is, however, almost inconceivable that the Indians alone put an end to the whole vast horse population of the late Pleistocene over so enormous an area.

This seems at present one of the situations in which we must be humble and honest and admit that we simply do not know the answer. It must be remembered too that extinction of the horses in the New World is only part of a larger problem. Many other animals became extinct here at about the same time. The general cause of extinction then or at earlier times must have been the occurrence of changes to which the animal populations could not adapt themselves. But what precisely were those changes? And why could not the horses (ground-sloths, mastodons, dire-wolves, et cetera) adapt to them, while many other groups of animals could?

19

THE HORSE'S RELATIVES

EVERYTHING that lives is related in some degree to the horse. A complete study of its relatives, or those of any other animal or plant must finally embrace the whole realm of life, a scope too ambitious for this modest book. Even the casual enquirer, however, will want to know something about the horse's really close relatives. We may at least point these out and name them, without attempting to follow their own complicated histories. They are summarized in Fig. 21.

The closest relatives of the horse, which yet are not themselves placed in the horse family, are the palaeotheres, already mentioned in passing as the more progressive European descendants of eohippus. In the later Eocene there were at least six quite distinct lines. It has been customary to group these all as palaeotheres in a general sense, members of a family Palaeotheriidae (pay'-lee-oh-the-rye'-id-ee), and to consider all as nearly horses. In fact, however, they are highly diverse and some have special resemblances to families other than the horses. The most conservative line, typified by *Pachynolophus* (pack-ee-noll'-oh-fuss), remained so like eohippus that it might be considered a group of European Eocene horses, parallel to our *Hyracotherium* → *Orohippus* → *Epihippus* line.

Palaeotherium (pay'-lee-oh-thee'-ree-um) itself is an extremely interesting genus of fossils from several different points of view. It was among the first fossils to be studied in detail and in a truly scientific manner. Many teeth and bones and even complete skeletons were found in the Montmartre gypsum within the city of Paris. Around the beginning of the nineteenth century these were studied

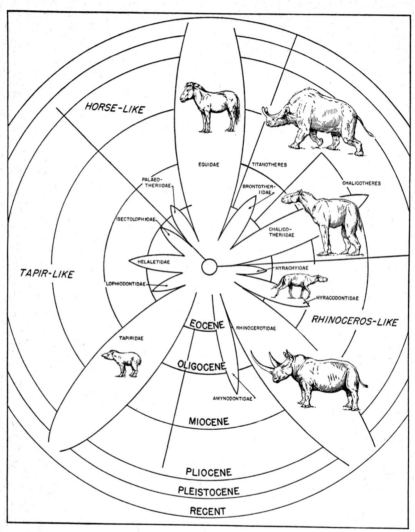

21. Adaptive radiation of horse relatives. The Order Perissodactyla arose as primitive animals similar to eohippus and evolved into a large number of divergent types. The oldest forms are shown in the center and progressively younger descendants radiating out from this in all directions.

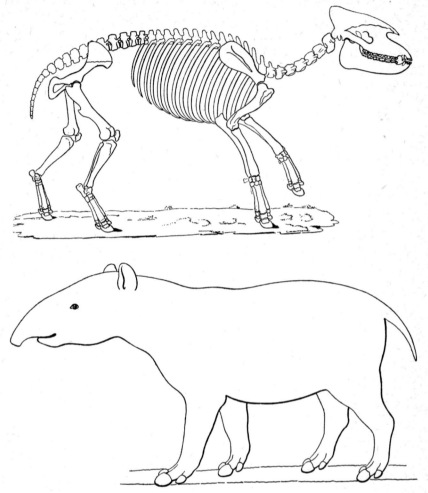

22. Cuvier's illustrations of *Palaeotherium*, first published in 1825. A reconstruction of the skeleton based on bones found in Montmartre, Paris, and an outline sketch of Cuvier's conception of the living animal. He may have made the animal look somewhat too much like a modern tapir.

by Cuvier (Baron Georges Léopold Chrétien Frédéric Dagobert Cuvier, to be exact) who, as much as any one person, was responsible for putting the science of paleontology on its feet. (See Fig. 22) This early entrance of *Palaeotherium* into the science accounts for the fact that it holds the name that to a paleontologist seems the most appropriate possible for a fossil mammal. *Palaeotherium* is coined

from two Greek words meaning 'ancient beast.' In several respects
these animals evolved faster than did the horses. Some of the later
species were as large as rhinoceroses. The teeth remained of browsing type, but by the end of the Eocene had achieved a perfection of
that adaptation not equaled by the horses until around the end of
the Oligocene. The canine teeth were larger than in any horses and
perhaps were used in fighting. The rather clumsy head was tapir-
like (although the teeth were more horse-like), and it may have had
a short trunk as in living tapirs. The body was stocky, the legs relatively short and stout, not adapted for particularly fast running.
Each foot had three large toes. The group survived into the early
Oligocene but then became extinct.

One other group, which lived in great numbers with *Palaeotherium* in the Eocene and became extinct with it in the early Oligocene,
deserves brief special mention. This is *Plagiolophus* (pladge-ee-oll'-
oh-fuss), sometimes called *Paloplotherium* (pay-lop'-lo-thee'-ree-um).
Its particular interest is that it rapidly developed moderately high-
crown, curved, strongly ridged, completely cement-covered teeth.
By the end of the Eocene it had reached a degree of grazing adaptation, or at least of ability to eat harsh, abrasive vegetation, not
achieved by the horses until middle or late Miocene. This difference
in timing is of value for the study of principles of evolution and
will be mentioned again when we come to consider those principles
in the light of horse history.

Relatives of horses in the next broader degree are the other animals that belong with it to the Order Perissodactyla (pair-iss'-oh-
dack'-till-ah). This order includes in general the more progressive
hoofed (ungulate) herbivorous mammals in which the central line
or main weight-bearing axis of the feet passes through the middle
toe (the third toe of the ancestral set of five).

There are, broadly, five different groups of animals in this order,
three of which have living representatives and two of which are
wholly extinct. (Fig. 21) One of the three groups with some survivors comprises the horses and palaeotheres. The two extinct groups
probably arose from an ancestor similar to eohippus and were rather
closely related to horses and palaeotheres, although they evolved into

quite different types. The titanotheres (tie'-tan-oh-theers') evolved relatively rapidly into great beasts of elephant size, with heavy heads armed with large, horn-like bony knobs on the nose. (Plate XXXa) The teeth and feet remained remarkably primitive. There were four toes on the forefeet and three on the hindfeet, as in eohippus, but the feet became short, broad, and heavy to carry the great, bulky body. The teeth remained low-crowned, of browsing type but without much real progress toward the most effective types of browsing teeth. The discrepancy between the increasingly large body and the rather inefficient apparatus for feeding it may have a bearing on the early extinction of the titanotheres. They occur throughout the Eocene in North America and spread in numbers through Eurasia, but all died out during the Oligocene.

In the other extinct group, the chalicotheres (calico-theres) (Plate XXXb), the teeth were also unprogressive and resembled those of the titanotheres rather closely, although the skull as a whole was more horse-like. The body was short and the front legs were longer than the hind legs, giving the animal an odd, ungainly look. The most extraordinary thing about these animals is that the hoof-like and eohippus-like nails on the toes of the earliest forms instead of developing into specialized hooves, as in horses and almost all other relatives, developed into large claws.

Claws and teeth were found separately by bonediggers before they were found together. They were given different names and it was considered absurd to suppose that they could belong to one sort of animal. In fact this violated what was then supposed to be one of the basic laws of nature: that of the correlation of parts; for instance, that similar teeth will always be associated with similar feet. This principle was a favorite of the great early paleontologist Cuvier, who first expressed it and who ardently supported it. His devotion to the principle was responsible for the widespread and, alas, quite mistaken belief that paleontologists can reconstruct whole animals from a single bone. But nature seems to delight in breaking her own laws, or what men think up as nature's laws. Nature might have concocted the chalicotheres as a joke on Cuvier and his followers. When it was finally established that the great chalicothere claws really do belong to animals with herbivorous dentitions, paleonthologists gave up forever their belief that they could reconstruct unknown parts of animals from a known fragment.

No living animals have this sort of tooth-foot combination, and the use of the claws is a real puzzle. Perhaps as good a guess as any is that they were used to dig up bulbs and tubers for food. If they did have access to some such special food supply, this would help to explain why they outlasted the titanotheres in spite of having, apparently, equally ineffectual teeth. They appeared in the Eocene of North America and Eurasia. In America they became extinct during the Miocene, but in Eurasia they survived into the Pliocene and were even present in the Pleistocene in warm regions in Asia and Africa.

The two living groups most nearly related to the horses are the tapirs and the rhinoceroses. (Plate XXXIa, b) Both were characterized by the early development of efficient browsing dentitions with sharp, continuous cross crests on both upper and lower teeth. Even in the Eocene the tapirs achieved such perfect adaptation to a particular way of life that they have retained it ever since without much change. The tapirs of today could almost be called living Eocene animals. They are larger than eohippus and so have somewhat heavier legs and feet, but they have four toes in front and three on the hind-feet as in eohippus, and the structure is in general remarkably like that small ancient horse. Their one really noteworthy peculiarity is that they have developed a proboscis somewhat like an elephant's trunk but much shorter.

In the Eocene there were many different kinds of tapirs and tapir-like animals, but from the Oligocene on there were only forms closely similar to those now living. They occurred widely in Eurasia and North America and were fairly common in what is now the United States even at the end of the Pleistocene. They survive, however, only in tropical parts of southeastern Asia and Central to South America.

Rhinoceros history was much more complex than that of the tapirs and involved repeated branching and progressive evolution along various different lines. North America was one of the centers of rhinoceros evolution from the Eocene, but they became extinct here before the end of the Pliocene. They were abundant throughout the Cenozoic (except its earliest stages) in the Old World. There were running rhinoceroses quite like three-toed horses in general build. Others were heavy, amphibious, hippopotamus-like forms. There were giants like *Baluchitherium,* largest known land mammal, standing 18 feet high at the shoulders. Most rhinoceroses were browsers but there were also grazing types, including one that carried this sort of tooth adaptation as far as did any of the grazing horses. Most rhinoceroses were hornless, but horns did develop repeatedly and in different ways. Some rhinoceroses had a pair of horns side by side, others two horns one in front of the other, others one horn on the tip of the nose, and others one horn farther back, on the forehead.

Although they have fewer local forms, living rhinoceroses are more fundamentally varied than are the horses and are referred to four different genera. The Indian and closely related Javanese rhinoceroses have a single horn. The three quite distinct Sumatran, African black, and African white rhinoceroses all have two horns, one behind the other, much longer in the African than in the Sumatran types. The white rhinoceros, which is not really white but only a paler gray, has high crowns on the cheek teeth.

20

FALSE HORSES

IN South America there formerly lived two groups of animals that were not horses and were not at all closely related to horses but which went through some closely similar evolutionary stages. Starting from ancestors sharply distinct from eohippus, they reached some of the same results that are seen in various lines of horses. They add some information with a bearing on how horses evolved, and they pose some special puzzles. Comparison of their history with that of horses contributes greatly to materials for the study of evolution in general. Their history is a different story and a long one, but some of its main points will be mentioned briefly.

When these groups developed, there were no horses in South America. It was still an island continent, which horses could not reach. These groups can, then, be considered as acquiring the horses' way of life and filling horses' places in nature in the absence of horses themselves. This sort of development is called parallel evolution, and it has occurred many times in the history of life and among many different groups of animals and plants.

In one of these groups, the Notohippidae (note'-o-hip'-id-ee), grazing teeth were developed. The incisors and canines formed a cropping apparatus much as in the horses, but with grooves instead of pits on the crowns. The molars became very high-crowned, the enamel formed an elaborate grinding pattern, different from that of the horse but working the same way, and the crowns became covered with cement. A particularly interesting point is that these animals had already in the Oligocene reached a degree of grazing-tooth spe-

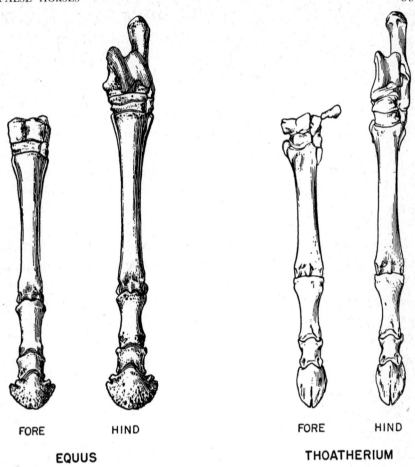

FORE   HIND   FORE   HIND

EQUUS   **THOATHERIUM**

23. Feet of a true, one-toed horse (*Equus*, left) and of a one-toed, South American pseudo-horse (*Thoatherium*, right). Drawn same size, not to scale, for comparison; the pseudo-horse is really considerably smaller.

cialization that the horses did not achieve until millions of years later, around the beginning of the Pliocene.

The other group, the Proterotheriidae (pro′-ter-o-thee-rye′-id-ee), retained browsing teeth throughout its history. There was no parallel to the later horses in the evolution of the dentition, but the skull and particularly the body and legs were very horse-like. (Plate XXXIIa) The legs became specialized for running in a way much like the swifter horses. In one line, three toes were retained, as they were in most horses, with the middle toe large and the side toes becoming somewhat reduced. Another line became one-toed, as in the *Plio-hippus-Equus* line of horses. These proterotheres and the horses are the only truly one-toed animals known. (Fig. 23) The reduction of the side toes was carried even farther than in horses, because in *Equus* they are still represented by rather long splint bones while in these South Americans they had become mere nubbins of bone.

The proterotheres reached the one-toed stage at the beginning of the Miocene, the horses not until much later, in the Pliocene, and the proterotheres had even more specialized feet in the Miocene than horses do today. Another peculiar point is that these one-toed proterotheres were not a very successful type. They soon became extinct, long before true horses came to South America. They are also interesting because they present a combination of foot and tooth types that never developed in the horses: they were one-toed brows-ers. Horses include three-toed browsers, three-toed grazers, and one-toed grazers, but no one-toed browsers.

Part Three

HORSES AND EVOLUTION

21

EVIDENCE IN COURT

THE story has been told how the little eohippus became the ancestor of Dobbin and the ancestor too of asses, onagers, and zebras, of *Hypohippus, Hipparion,* and *Hippidion.* The story has been pieced together over a period of generations by the labors of hundreds of devoted workers, seeking for bones weeks on end under blazing suns in many lands, quarrying by the month to amass the fossils embedded in the rocks, and patiently piecing and reconstructing through the years in the laboratories of museums and universities, great and small. Thoughtful men have devoted whole lifetimes to examining these remains, classifying them, ordering them in sequence, and seeking to interpret their evidence on the mysteries of life.

Why have so many able men been willing to devote their best years to this search? And why have their backers, hard-headed businessmen in many cases, been willing to provide large sums for the discovery and study of fragments of animals long dead?

Simple curiosity is part of the answer. Many scientific discoveries, probably most of the more fundamental discoveries, have been made because a scientist was curious and had a good idea how to set about satisfying his curiosity. The desire to know about everything under the sun is a peculiarly and admirably human trait and it is not confined to the professional scientist. A Stanford wants to know how his horses trot, so he buys camera lenses for a Muybridge. His curiosity is satisfied (and, for better or for worse, he has helped to bring the motion picture into being). A Whitney is curious about how his horses came to be the great running machines that they are, so he gives an Osborn support for a campaign of fossil collecting in the badlands of the West. He is gratified to see the results unfold as a series of ancestral skeletons in our great museum. Impelled by curiosity, crowds throng to see the strange little eohippus and its descendants. The support of these crowds, most important of all, approves the maintenance in our society of museums and other research institutions.

There are, however, other and stronger motives for the search, and it has other and more important results than entertainment and the satisfaction of curiosity, worth while as these are.

The men who first worked out, in broad outlines, the history of the horse family were interested above all in testing the theory of evolution, a theory that has had most profound effects on all branches of human learning and philosophy. The ideas that one species may, in the course of time, be transformed into another, that the marvelous diversity of life on earth today may have developed gradually by modification and descent from simple beginnings, and that all these forms of life may be physically akin—these ideas have repeatedly occurred to naturalists and philosophers for centuries. They had been expressed at considerable length long before Darwin, but the evidence available in earlier days was not sufficient either to prove or to disprove these ideas. Darwin's work brought together a larger amount of evidence than had previously been compiled. It convinced most open-minded students that the general idea of evolution is the true key to the history of life. It also suggested ways for further testing of the truth of this theory and methods of learning more and useful principles of how evolution occurs.

There are many different sorts of evidence bearing on evolution. On the main point, consideration of the basic question whether evolution has or has not in fact occurred, Darwin had already marshalled evidence of all the most important sorts. He pointed to the variations of domestic animals and the origin of new kinds by selective breeding and experimentation. He saw that similar variations exist in wild animals and that their races may be closely analogous to breeds. He observed that many features of the geographic distribution of animals and plants over the face of the earth are explained if we suppose that their diversity and resemblances are the result of evolution. It was, indeed, observations of this sort, made as a young man when he sailed around the earth on the surveying ship *Beagle,* that converted Darwin from a special-creationist to an evolutionist.

Darwin also considered at length the anatomy of animals and plants and showed that the structural resemblances and differences between various groups likewise bear strong testimony to the truth of evolution. Many anatomical characters are closely related to their uses, and different organs may be modified for similar uses, like the wings of birds and of insects, which are analogical in Darwin's phrase. (We call them analogous.) In other cases, structures clearly correspond and seem to have some common origin (we now call them homologous) but may have different uses, like the wings of birds and the arms of men. There are also vestigial structures, like the buried tail vertebrae (the coccyx) in man, with no present function but clearly homologous with structures in more or less similar animals (in this case with the tails of monkeys and lower mammals), in which they do have uses. There are thousands of facts of this sort that are fully comprehensible under the theory of evolution but that seem meaningless and capricious under any other view. Similar evidence arises from consideration of the development of individual organisms from egg or seed to adult, and from the comparison of this process in different sorts of animals and plants.

All such lines of evidence have been explored much farther since Darwin's day, and innumerable facts unknown to him have been added. All the new facts agree fully with his main conclusion, that evolution is the key to the history of life. On this point and in these fields his accumulated evidence already seemed to his more open-minded contemporaries, and still seems to us, to be conclusive. Yet when Darwin came to consider one other necessary line of evidence, that of the fossils, he struck a snag.

The most direct sort of evidence on the truth of evolution must, after all, be provided by the fossil record. The theory postulates that life has changed gradually (in all probability) but profoundly during the millions of years of earth history. Clearly, then, the theory can and should be tested by learning what life has been like in successive periods of that history. If life is found to have changed from one period to another, and if the changes are such as to suggest that the animals and plants of a given time are the modified descendants of those of previous times, then the theory will be supported. If many observations of this kind are made and all agree so well with the theory that no other explanation is reasonable, then the theory may be taken as proved, for all practical purposes. If, on the other hand, no marked differences were found between the life of earlier and that of later ages, then the theory of evolution would seem unlikely and the theory of one special creation and fixity of species would be supported. If the life of successive ages differed suddenly and radically and earlier ages revealed no likely ancestors for the animals and plants of later ages, then also the theory of evolution in its usual form would become improbable and some other theory, perhaps of evolution by widespread saltation or of successive special creations, would be suggested.

Darwin and his contemporaries saw that this sort of evidence would be crucial for evolution. In *The Origin of Species* Darwin devoted two chapters (x and xi) to this subject. He was able to show that what was then known of the history of life was consistent with the theory of evolution, but he was forced to admit that knowledge was far too incomplete to give conclusive support to this theory. He saw that the fossil record, if more complete, should provide graded ancestral series for the animals of today and intermediates between our different species and distinct higher groups. He could only conclude, honestly but sadly, that, 'Geology assuredly does not reveal any such finely-graduated organic chain; and this, perhaps, is the most obvious and serious objection which can be urged against the theory.'

It was, and it still is, hopeless to expect to find every intermediate in every 'organic chain,' or even the greater number of them. To do so, we should have to find remains of most of the uncounted millions of sorts of animals and plants of the past, and this is quite impossible. Most of these have vanished completely and are not preserved by any trace anywhere on earth. Of those that are preserved somewhere, we have so far found and studied only a small fraction. Many of the reasons for the inevitable imperfection of our knowledge were well expressed by Darwin, and others are fairly obvious. Yet if evolution is true, and if search is made widely and intensively for fossils, some—eventually many—examples of graded series of ancestors and descendants should be found. None of clear significance had yet been found when Darwin published his theory, and he was right in thinking this the 'most obvious and serious objection' to that theory.

No wonder, then, the paleontologists of the nineteenth century, after 1859 (when *The Origin of Species* was published), were especially concerned with trying to find series of fossils of different ages that would prove or disprove the theory of evolution. The greatest of their earlier successes was in finding fossils demonstrating the main lines of descent in the horse family from eohippus to the living horse. We are still filling in some of the details, but before 1900 the evidence was complete enough to show in the most convincing way that *Equus* had, in fact, evolved from a radically different little animal that lived in the early Eocene. From providing the most obvious and serious objection to the theory of evolution, paleontology had progressed to the point of providing the most convincing of all proofs of that theory.

In our younger days many of us heard the late William Jennings Bryan thunder against the theory of evolution, which he never really studied or understood but against which he harbored a bigot's rancor. Brilliant in manner and clever in expression, but with no concern for factual evidence or honest logic, Bryan, in one of his most telling wisecracks, said that he would believe in the theory of evolution when he could sit down in his garden and see an onion turn into a lily! As a bit of reasoning, this is just as silly as if he had said that he would believe that the Marx brothers had the same mother when he saw Groucho turn into Harpo.

As a matter of fact, if Mr. Bryan had really wanted to learn the truth about evolution, he could have seen something stranger and more convincing than an onion turning into a lily; he could have seen eohippus turn into *Equus*. The difference between them is much greater than that between an onion and a lily, and yet when the fossils are laid out in proper sequence there is an almost continuous gradation through time from the earlier to the later form. This sequence is well exemplified in the public exhibits of many museums (some of which are listed in an appendix to this book).

Even these exhibits give an inadequate idea how convincing the evidence really is. An exhibit necessarily shows only a few individual specimens. Two individuals always differ from each other; even father and son are never quite alike. The complete demonstration of the descent of *Equus* from eohippus lies in studying whole populations of successive ages by comparing dozens or hundreds of specimens from each, as preserved in the research collections of our museums. Each population varies considerably, as populations always do. The most convincing feature of the horse family as evidence of evolution is that throughout most of their history the variations demonstrated in collections of successive ages overlap: the ancestral and descendant populations intergrade completely in this way. There is still one gap where overlap is not quite complete (between *Epihippus* and *Mesohippus*), and there are some other points where more material is needed on the level of relatively unimportant details in regard to species, but the sequence is now so well represented that it leaves no doubt whatsoever about the main fact in the mind of anyone who studies it extensively.

The history of the horse family is still one of the clearest and most convincing for showing that organisms really have evolved, for demonstrating that, so to speak, an onion can turn into a lily. Many other histories, more or less complete, have, however, now been compiled from the fossil record. These involve an extremely wide variety, samples from all parts of the plant and animal kingdoms—ferns, grasses, oaks, microscopic one-celled animals, clams, snails, fishes, dinosaurs, camels, elephants, and many others. Paleontological demonstration of the truth of evolution can now be based about as well on any of a hundred or more different families as on the horse family.

This is done. There really is no point nowadays in continuing to collect and to study fossils simply to determine whether or not evolution is a fact. The question has been decisively answered in the affirmative. There are still those who deny this, of course—there are still some who deny that the earth is round. It is no use gathering more evidence to persuade these doubters, because the evidence already in hand has convinced everyone who ever really studied it. Anyone who cannot or will not accept or attempt to understand this evidence is not likely to have the will or the ability to evaluate new facts of the same sort.

Then why go on? Why is the search for fossils more intensive now than ever, and why are so many students still devoting their lives to this subject? There are three main reasons among a number of less importance. One, most immediate and obvious but in the long run the least impelling of the three, is that fossils are extensively used in geological studies many of which have a dollars-and-cents value, especially in the search for petroleum. The fossil horses have a bearing in this field, although in this respect they are not essential and are far exceeded in importance by many fossils, shells and the like, less spectacular and less interesting for their own sake.

The second, and more important, main reason for continuing the search is to increase our knowledge of the earth and of its life. Since evolution is a fact and since we ourselves and everything in the world about us are products of an evolutionary history, comprehension of our own lives and guidance in them demand as much information as possible regarding the history of our planet and of life on it. We now know the main outlines of that history. We shall never know all its details, because parts of the record have certainly been lost beyond recall. But we only know a small fraction of what it is clearly possible to know, and increasing that fraction is one of the most exciting and one of the most fundamental things to which a scientist can devote himself.

The final and probably most important of the main reasons for continuing the search concerns the study of the principles and processes of evolution, aside from the history of what has occurred in the course of evolution. The preceding discussion of the bearing of the horses and other organisms, fossil and recent, on evolution has referred to the relatively simple, nineteenth-century problem of whether or not evolution has occurred. We want and need to know a great deal more than this; we want to know also how and why evolution has occurred, the latter is a far more difficult and complex problem, one that is by no means fully solved.

There is essentially only one theory of evolution in general, and the question regarding it, 'True or false?' has been answered. There are many theories about the hows and whys of evolution; few of them can be dismissed simply as true or as false; and there is still doubt which theory or, more likely, which combination of theories offers the best explanation.

Attempts to explain evolution are as old as the general idea of evolution. In the eighteenth century a possible explanation was advanced by the French naturalist Buffon, whose works are still being reprinted in France, where they grace the bookshelves in all cultured homes. Around and shortly after the beginning of the nineteenth century, the still greater French naturalist Lamarck proposed another explanation, especially in a work that happened to be published in the year of Charles Darwin's birth, 1809. (Incidentally, it is an even more striking coincidence that Darwin was born not only in the same year but also on the same day as Abraham Lincoln.) Charles Darwin's own grandfather, Erasmus Darwin, had also proposed an explanation that resembled Lamarck's in some respects and was earlier. These and other early attempts to explain evolution were highly speculative because too few facts were then known.

Darwin's work was devoted not only to the question whether evolution occurs but also to an attempt to explain its occurrence. He reviewed other possibilities and accepted some of them as partial explanations, but he particularly stressed natural selection as a cause of evolution. It is this theory, in the form proposed by Darwin, to which the name 'Darwinism' correctly applies. Some who are not specialists in the subject have used 'Darwinism' as if it were synonymous with 'evolution,' instead of being the name of one of numerous proposed and possible *explanations* of evolution. This has caused much confusion, and the arguments about Darwinism have incorrectly been supposed to be arguments about the truth of evolution.

Many firm believers in evolution have rejected Darwinism as an explanation of evolution.

Much has been learned about possible causes and processes of evolution since Darwin. His own theory has been modified by his followers, other theories have been developed, and the whole field of study has been made richer and more complicated. There has been revolutionary progress in the study of heredity, about which there was little exact knowledge in Darwin's time. The great advance in knowledge of fossils has also made important new contributions. The success of these efforts up to now and the need for still more facts bearing on evolutionary theories are the main purely scientific incentives for continued and wider collection and study of fossils.

The evolution of the horse has an essential bearing on the study of the how and why of evolution, and a book on the horse family would be incomplete without some discussion of this. The history of the family has already been given in terms of the various sorts of horses, what they were like, when and where they lived, and their relationships of ancestry and descent—what is known as the phylogeny of the family. It is now proposed to summarize the changes brought about by evolution in the various parts of the anatomy of the horse, a subject that sometimes rejoices in the name of morphogeny. This concludes consideration of the 'what' of evolution as far as horses are concerned. Then both the family history and the anatomical history, phylogeny and morphogeny, will be called on for evidence on the 'how' of evolution, its general outlines and pattern. In a final chapter, some of the more important attempts to decipher the 'why' of evolution, particularly that of Darwin and those made since Darwin, will be briefly summarized. The evidence of the horse family on this most fundamental of all the problems of the history of life will be reviewed, and the present status of the problem suggested.

22

HOW HORSES CHANGED:
SKULL AND BRAIN

As eohippus changed to *Equus* and, in branching lines, to *Hypohippus*, to *Hipparion*, to *Hippidion*, and to various other late genera, the whole body was profoundly altered. There is no anatomical part of any of these advanced forms of horses that is not obviously different from the same part in eohippus. The changes took place at varying rates. Some features changed rather rapidly, and then practically ceased to evolve. Others continued more or less steadily over long epochs. Some changes occurred in one line of descent and not in others. Sometimes the same sorts of changes went on independently in different lines. All these changes in the forms and functions of different anatomical parts are essential features of the 'what' of horse evolution, its description as a series of historical events. The way in which such changes occurred is also good evidence from which may be deduced something of the 'how' and 'why' of evolution in general.

It is convenient to summarize these changes as if each part were evolving separately, so that we speak of 'the evolution of the teeth,' 'the evolution of the feet,' and so on, as separate topics. Remember, however, that the whole animal was evolving, and that an animal is an organism. It is called that because its parts are organized into a unit, the whole body, and no part can operate in complete independence from any other part. At all stages in the history of the horse family the animals as a whole were well integrated and the animals as a whole evolved. Eohippus was not an imperfect model that needed to have the teeth, feet, and other parts rebuilt to make it into *Equus*. Eohippus was a going concern on its own, a well-adapted animal that got along very well in its own world and following its own habits. Markedly different forms, like *Equus,* eventually arose from eohippus by changes of the organism as a whole meeting changing conditions and acquiring different abilities and ways of life.

It would be a lengthy affair and of little interest except to the specialist if we were to follow through the changes in all detail or for all parts of the body. In any case, the available material would not suffice to do this literally. The fossil remains consist of bones and teeth only, and seldom of all these for any one individual. Some soft parts can be reconstructed with some accuracy from the bones. The leg muscles and tendons, for instance, leave marks on the bones where they are attached, and, still more valuable, the brain follows closely although not precisely the modeling of the interior of the cranium. Other soft parts, such as the stomach or heart, leave no traces in the fossil remains.

In the selection of important anatomical features in which evolutionary changes may be briefly described, the obvious first choice is the head as a whole and more particularly the brain and the teeth. The importance of the brain is evident; it is the central co-ordinating organ of the body and its evolution has been an essential factor in the evolution of most higher mammals, especially in man but also in the horse. The teeth are inherently important because they play an essential part in obtaining food, one of the most basic activities of all living things. The nature of the food used, evolutionary changes in diet, and the efficiency of food gathering and preparation can be judged, within limits, from the teeth. They are also of special and practical interest in dealing with fossils, because of all parts of the body of most mammals, and specifically of horses, they are most likely to be preserved and are most easily recognized and classified.

Next in interest come the limbs, and in the limbs the most indicative parts are usually their lower ends, the feet. Locomotion is another of the most important activities of most mammals, essential in finding food or opportunities for mating, and a background for almost every activity except sheer relaxation—if that can be called an activity. In horses, locomotion has been particularly important because they are among the animals that escape from their numerous enemies mainly by fleetness of foot. If they do come to grips with an enemy or a rival, the feet are also their principal weapons. The teeth are sometimes used as second-line weapons, but they are not well adapted for this purpose in horses, and this use has apparently had little to do with their evolution.

The structures to which special attention is to be given are, then, the head as a whole, but particularly the brain and the teeth, and the limbs as a whole, but particularly the feet.

The outstanding features of the evolution of the head of the horse are rather simple, in spite of innumerable changes or fluctuations of detail and in spite of the more complex history of some of the organs, such as the teeth, included in the head. (See Fig. 24) In eohippus as seen from the side the eye is almost in the middle of the head. The face, in front of the eye, is of almost the same length as the cranium, behind the eye. In later horses these proportions change markedly, although not rapidly. In *Equus* the face is about twice as long as the cranium. This radical difference in proportions is a main reason why the head of eohippus, properly restored, does not look simply like a small horse's head.

It has been found that this change in proportions is rather closely connected with the size of the head. At any one time, smaller individual horses tend to have the eyes relatively farther forward than in their large relatives. Horses with heads of about the same size tend to have the proportions about the same, even though some are of later age and in other respects have evolved farther. This is a case, one of many now known, in which the progressive evolution of one character is only apparent or is secondary and is closely linked to change in another character evidently more basic. Progressive enlargement of the head was the rule in horse evolution, even though it was not constant in rate and the opposite occasionally occurred. Change in head proportions accompanied these changes in size. (Fig. 25)

Other changes, most of them less closely correlated with size, also took place at the same time. The premaxillas, the bones that

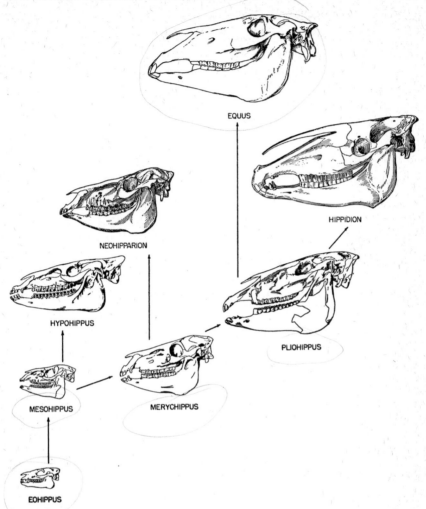

24. Evolutionary series of horse skulls. Only a few genera representing various lines are shown. See Fig. 13 to see how they fit into the family as a whole. Drawn to scale.

carry the upper front teeth (incisors), tended to protrude more. The nasal bones, along the top of the nose, came to project as a sort of spike, but not to reach as far forward, relatively, as in eohippus. These changes were related to the development of the flexible muzzle so characteristic of the modern horse. The sides of the face also became deeper, as was necessary in the grazing horses to lodge their deep, prismatic grinding teeth. In some horses pits were developed on the sides of the face and then were lost again in some of their descendants.

In eohippus, as in the most primitive mammals, the eye socket was not circled by bone, but was open behind. Later a projection grew from the top of the skull (frontal) behind the eye and another

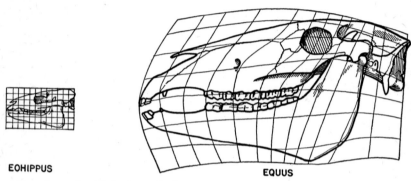

EOHIPPUS

EQUUS

25. Transformation of the horse skull, from eohippus to *Equus*. The skull of eohippus is drawn on a grid of squares. The skull of *Equus* is drawn on a grid in which the various lines and intersections have the same anatomical positions as in the eohippus grid. Differential enlargement of the squares and distortion of the lines reveal changes in proportions and shape in the course of evolution.

from the cheek arch (zygoma) below this. These met and formed a bar of bone, closing the eye socket, retained in all the later horses. Such an arrangement protects the eye and also makes the whole skull more rigid and better able to support stresses and strains.

Not only did the cranium become relatively shorter in the later, larger horses, but also it tended to become wider, more globular, and larger in absolute dimensions. These reflect more important changes that were going on inside the skull, in the brain. The evolution of the brain has not yet been worked out in full detail, because, numerous as fragmentary fossil horses are, well-preserved skulls suitable for dissection are still rare for some stages and lacking for others. The main points, however, have recently been put together (by Tilly Edinger, published in 1948). (See Fig. 26)

The brain itself, soft tissue that decays very rapidly, is not preserved in any fossil horse and study is really based on the cavity

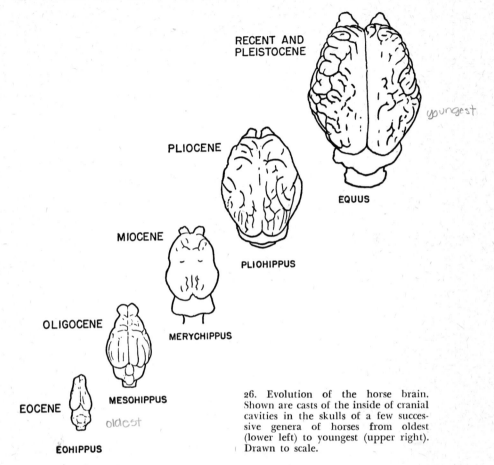

RECENT AND PLEISTOCENE

youngest

EQUUS

PLIOCENE

PLIOHIPPUS

MIOCENE

MERYCHIPPUS

OLIGOCENE

MESOHIPPUS

EOCENE

EOHIPPUS

oldest

26. Evolution of the horse brain. Shown are casts of the inside of cranial cavities in the skulls of a few successive genera of horses from oldest (lower left) to youngest (upper right). Drawn to scale.

formerly occupied by the brain. This reflects most of the important features of the brain, although minor details may be obscure or lacking. Sometimes the cavity became filled with mud after the brain had decayed and as the skull was buried. Hardened into rock, this filling may provide an excellent natural cast of the brain cavity. In other cases the cavity can be cleaned out in the laboratory and a rubber or gelatin cast made which can be reproduced in plaster for study and permanent preservation.

The most remarkable feature of the story of the horse brain, thus established, is at the beginning. In spite of its antiquity and many distinctive peculiarities, eohippus is often thought of as

simply a little horse. Most people would have guessed that it had a
horse brain, smaller and simpler than in *Equus* probably, but still
distinctive of the brainy horse family. This is not the case. Eohippus
turns out to have one of the most primitive brains known in any
mammal. There is nothing horse-like about its brain, which more
closely resembles the brain of a reptile or of the most primitive
mammals, such as the opossum, notorious for stupidity.

A primitive mammal brain, seen from the side, seems to consist
mainly of three rather lumpy and irregular parts stretched out in
a line one behind the other. In front is the smallest and simplest
part, the paired olfactory bulbs, concerned with nerves coming
from the nose and with the sense of smell. Next come the likewise
paired cerebral hemispheres, which are very complex in structure
and function even in the most primitive animals, but in which the
lower parts are mainly concerned with sensory and more or less
instinctive functions while the outer layers (cortex) of the upper
parts are more involved in association and functions related to intelligence. The most posterior main segment of the brain is the
cerebellum, which has a median, central part (vermis), and a complex of paired swellings on each side (mainly the cerebellar hemispheres or paramedian lobes). This segment too is extremely complex in structure and function, but it is little concerned, directly,
with conscious or intelligent behavior and has to do mainly with
motor and motor-sensory co-ordination of the various parts of the
body.

The most important feature of brain evolution among mammals is the development of the part especially concerned in intelligence, the outer layers of the upper part of the cerebrum, called
the neocortex. Expansion of the neocortex is clearly required for
the evolution of intelligent behavior and is correlated with higher
types of mental functioning. It reaches an extreme in man, and is
also, but less, well developed in the more intelligent subhumans,
especially apes and also dogs, horses, and other fairly intelligent
mammals. This expansion takes place in two ways, by absolute or
relative increase in the size of the cerebrum, and by wrinking of
its upper surface. Development of numerous fissures on this region

increases the surface area, which is the essential point, even without any increase in the volume of the cerebrum.

In eohippus, neocortex expansion either in size or by fissuring had hardly begun, and this is the most striking and primitive feature of the brain of that animal. The cerebrum was already the largest part of the brain, as it is in reptiles and many lower animals, but it was much smaller, relative, especially, to the olfactory bulbs, than in later horses or other mentally progressive mammals. The upper part, the neocortex, was small, only slightly swollen, no higher and barely wider than the cerebellum. It was almost smooth. Only three small fissures or sulci can be seen. In eohippus the cerebellum also was much simpler and less fissured than in later horses, or most other mammals. Another very primitive feature is that there is a gap between cerebellum and cerebrum and an intermediate part of the brain (midbrain) could still be seen here when the brain was viewed from above.

Eohippus must have been an extraordinarily stupid animal. Edinger remarks: 'The brain connects eohippus only with the past. The ancestral brain, an unspecialized mammalian brain, was held over in the equid body. No feature of this brain signals the future.'

Brains of later Eocene horses are very poorly known, but there is evidence that the brain was rapidly evolving at that time. This is remarkable in view of the fact that almost no change was then occurring in size, feet, or general skeletal characters, and only a little in the teeth. By the Oligocene, where the brain of *Mesohippus* is unusually well known, the main steps had been taken and the brain was already recognizably that of a horse. The cerebrum as a whole, and especially its important upper part, had expanded greatly. It had completely covered the midbrain and had overlapped part of the cerebellum. It was also well fissured, with all the main sulci of the modern horse brain. It was, nevertheless, still distinctly more primitive than in the later and recent horses. The rich branching of main sulci and development of secondary sulci had not yet occurred. The expanded cerebrum was still relatively smaller than it was to become. The olfactory bulbs were still prominent and not overlapped by the cerebrum.

After *Mesohippus,* advance to the brain of *Equus* apparently
continued rather steadily, although there was a time of relatively
rapid change in the genus *Merychippus,* middle to late Miocene.
(It is interesting that the teeth were also evolving relatively rapidly
in these same animals.) The cerebrum and especially its neocortex
continued to increase in size and to develop more complex fissures.
The cerebellum also became larger and more complex, although
its increase in size was overshadowed by that of the cerebrum. The
front of the cerebrum overrode the olfactory bulbs, so that these
came to lie obscurely near the base of the front of the brain. The
olfactory bulbs did not progress in any definite way, but they were
not reduced, and the sense of smell, with which they are primarily
concerned, continues to be important in the modern horse, as it
was in eohippus.

23

HOW HORSES CHANGED: TEETH

THE history of the teeth is much the best-known feature of horse evolution and has been worked out in most elaborate detail, indeed in far too great detail for adequate summary in a general book like this. Attention will be confined to the main features of the evolution of the cheek teeth, the premolars, and molars. These teeth form one continuous series in horses and work together as a unit, the function of which is to crush and grind vegetable food. This preparation is necessary not only so that the food can be swallowed readily but also to start the processes of digestion by mixing food with saliva, and also, particularly, to break up the tough, almost indigestible cell walls of plant tissue so that the more digestible and nourishing cell contents become available.

Some types of plant food, such as succulent leaves, are easier to break up than others and so make less demand on the teeth. Grass is one of the hardest foods of all, because great quantities are needed and it contains harsh, abrasive mineral matter (silica), not to mention the fact that animals eating it are bound also to take in much grit and dust. The tooth requirements of plant-eating animals differ not only because of the different sorts of plants eaten, but also because of the different sizes of the animals. An animal twice as high as another tends to be not twice but approximately eight times as heavy. It then needs roughly eight times as much food in order to maintain this weight and to remain active. The teeth cannot meet the demand by simply increasing in size in proportion to the increase in body size. This would increase their area and approximate capacity only four times, which would be only half enough. The difficulty is increased by the fact that larger animals are, as a rule, slower to mature and longer of life. Their teeth must therefore last longer if the animals are to survive.

These two factors, type of food and adjustment of dentition to size, are the keys to the broad, adaptive changes in the cheek teeth of the horse family. Eohippus started out with cheek teeth adapted for eating the softer sorts only of leafy vegetation and for nourishing small animals during a short life span. Survival in later horses involved ability to eat a wider variety of foods or a change to a more available type and also increase in body size and length of life. The teeth of eohippus evidently served that animal well and were sufficiently adapted to its own needs. Changes in the descendants of eohippus, however, made new and increasing demands on the teeth and, unless these demands had been met, the animals would all have become extinct—as many of them did, whether for this reason alone, or for more complex reasons.

Such demands can be met in several different ways. One is to increase the total working surface of the teeth in proportion to the size of the animal. This was the first progressive development in the horse dentition after eohippus, long before the end of the history, but it reached a point beyond which further significant progress was impossible. There is a limit to the relative enlargement of teeth beyond which the proportions of head and jaws become unworkable. (Increase in the number of teeth, which did not occur among horses, would quickly run up against this same limitation and would be less effective in a plant eater than increase in size of the teeth already present.) Another way to meet increased demands on the teeth is for crushing and grinding to become more efficient, so that more food can be prepared in a given time per unit of tooth area. This can occur by changes of pattern, such as the development of crests instead of separate cusps and also by complication of the pattern so that a greater length of ridges, the grinding elements, is crowded into the same area. Changes of this sort were in progress at various times in most of the lines of descent in the horse family. Increase in complication was especially characteristic at times in the most progressive lines. This not only permitted preparation of more food in a given time but it also prolonged the usefulness of the teeth because a given amount of food resulted in less wear. Another way to prolong the effective life of the teeth is for them to become higher. With identical patterns and the same rate of use, the duration before the teeth are worn out obviously will depend on their height. Increase in height was also a frequent and important factor in evolution of horse teeth.

Increase in relative size of teeth, change in type of pattern, complication of pattern, and increase in crown height all occurred in horses and were the main changes in their teeth. They did not all occur in the same way or at the same time in different lines of descent, or at a constant rate in any one line. In dental evolution, as in the evolution of other parts, there was no single trend that occurred constantly in all horses and throughout the history of the family. It should also be emphasized that, although these adaptive features explain the main changes in the teeth, they do not explain all the fluctuations and changes in details. Minor differences in pattern characteristic of closely allied genera and species seem in some cases to have no particular adaptive value and to have arisen at random. These irregularities in horse evolution have commonly been overlooked or undervalued, and the bearing of the evidence on the principles of evolution has therefore sometimes been misunderstood.

A review of the changes that did occur in the cheek teeth of horses starts, of course, with eohippus. It had four premolars and three molars in each jaw. The first premolar was somewhat spaced and did not enter into the effective cheek-tooth series to any great extent. In fact this tooth, without being eliminated even now, never became an important part of the apparatus and did not evolve significantly. The other cheek teeth, six in each jaw, formed a series. All had very low crowns with simple patterns. The enamel was raised in ridges, but these were not sharply continuous and an ancestral pattern of separate cusps was still visible. The molars were somewhat squared. The premolars were smaller than the molars, more triangular, and had simpler patterns. Chewing depended mainly on the three molars.

FIRST   LAST
MOLAR   PREMOLARS

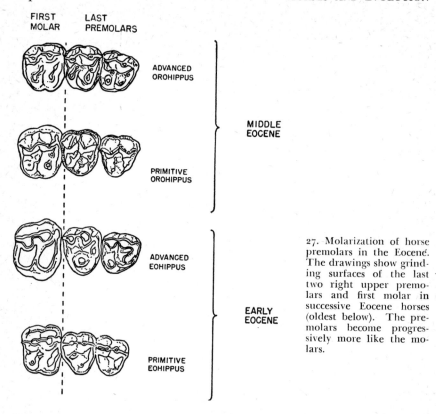

ADVANCED
OROHIPPUS

MIDDLE
EOCENE

PRIMITIVE
OROHIPPUS

ADVANCED
EOHIPPUS

EARLY
EOCENE

PRIMITIVE
EOHIPPUS

27. Molarization of horse premolars in the Eocene. The drawings show grinding surfaces of the last two right upper premolars and first molar in successive Eocene horses (oldest below). The premolars become progressively more like the molars.

During the later parts of the Eocene and into the Oligocene, the pattern of the molars changed somewhat, but not much. They became more sharply, continuously crested. The outer crest (ectoloph), on the cheek side of the upper molars, became W-shaped, a peculiarity already distinct in the late Eocene (*Epihippus*) and retained by all horses ever since. The most striking change that went on at this time was the molarization of the premolars, which means that the premolars were becoming relatively larger and more like the molars in pattern. (Fig. 27) Although it fluctuated considerably at all times, on the average this process went on at a rather steady rate. In the middle Eocene the last, fourth, premolar was nearly like a molar and the third was becoming so. In the late Eocene the fourth premolar was almost exactly like a molar, the third was nearly so, and the second was clearly on the way. In the Oligocene

Mesohippus, three premolars (all but the first, which never changed much) were like molars.

Already in the Oligocene, then, the horses had a grinding apparatus of six large, similar cheek teeth. This apparatus was more unified than in eohippus, and it had considerably more area in proportion to the space occupied in the jaw. Three of the premolars had become not only like the molars in pattern but also about as large as the molars. This sort of increase in capacity and efficiency had then gone about as far as it could. The only later change in this respect was that the premolars tended to become relatively somewhat larger still, so that in late horses the last three premolars are commonly, but only slightly, larger than the molars.

Mesohippus had a highly efficient set of browsing teeth, for eating a wide variety of plant food as long as it was relatively soft and did not wear the teeth down too rapidly. The cheek teeth did not change very markedly in any of the later horses that stuck to this general type of diet. Changes in pattern were almost neglible. Some of the crests became more fully united (union of ectoloph and metaloph) and in some lines, but not all, there was slight complication by development of small secondary spurs on the crests (small crochet on upper teeth). In the larger horses of this general browsing type, forms like *Hypohippus* and, especially, the giant *Megahippus,* the need for more durable teeth was met simply by increase in the height of the crowns. This increase is quite noticeable and evidently was sufficient to compensate for the greater food requirements and longer lives of larger animals, but it was not carried very far. The teeth are still to be designated technically as low-crowned or brachydont, that is, their height did not become notably greater than their length or width.

The imporance of the tooth changes that occurred in the *Parahippus-Merychippus* line has already been stressed in telling the story of the great transition that occurred in these horses during the Miocene. The change involved quite clearly a change in diet from browsing to grazing. After the new type of dentition was perfected, the animals could eat almost any vegetable food, including the harsh prairie grasses. These would have worn down the browsing teeth so rapidly that a browsing horse that ate much grass would have worn its teeth out at an early age and died prematurely. There is also some evidence that grass was becoming more abundant in the Miocene and that broad steppes and prairies were developing. Thus there was a new or more widespread environment and type of food that could be exploited by the horses that acquired teeth fit to cope with this food. There undoubtedly had to be changes in the digestive system as well as in the teeth. These changes are not recorded in the fossils, which preserve no traces of the soft viscera, and we can only infer that changes in these parts did accompany changes in the teeth.

In the line of horses that made this transition, evolution of the teeth during the Miocene was much more rapid than it was at any other time, before or since, or than it was then in any other line of horses. This rapid evolution involved three main changes, all going on at the same time: modification of pattern, increase of crown height, and development of cement. (See Fig. 28) In the upper cheek teeth, extension, connection, and complication of the enamel crests went on apace. There had been some slight similar tendency in the browsers immediately ancestral to *Parahippus,* but nothing like what now occurred. What had been two open valleys on the teeth now became deep, closed pits (prefossette and post-fossette). Numerous and variable wrinkles, side-crests, or spurs appeared on the sides of the main crests. Similar but less extreme changes occurred in the lower teeth. Their valleys became nearly but not quite closed, and some, but not so many, secondary folds developed.

Increase in tooth height was equally striking. Species of *Para-hippus* in the early Miocene were still browsing animals with low-crowned (brachydont) teeth. Species of *Merychippus* in the late Miocene were fully high-crowned (hypsodont), with the height of the crowns at least twice their length or width.

In the browsing horses, the tooth crowns had consisted of an outer layer of hard enamel and an inner core of softer dentine—the same tissues as in our own teeth. In late *Parahippus* and early *Merychippus* a new substance, cement, appeared on the teeth outside the enamel,

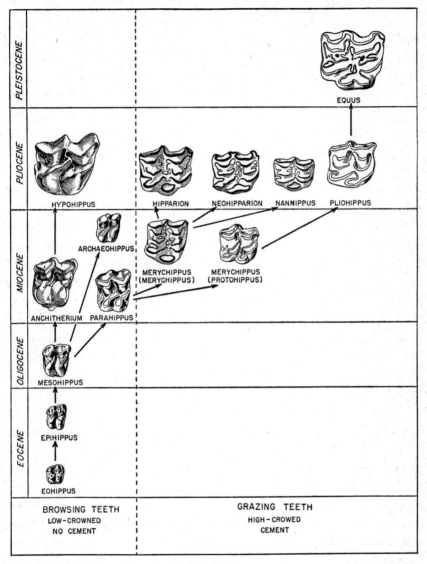

28. Evolution of horse teeth. Grinding surfaces of right upper molars in various genera. Drawn to scale.

and developed rapidly until it filled all the valleys or pits and heavily coated the outside of the crown. Cement, like dentine, is softer than enamel but it is firm, tough, and less brittle. If cement had not developed while the teeth were becoming so high-crowned, there would have been deep, open valleys and pits in which food would lodge and decay. The high, slender, brittle enamel crests, unsupported on either side, would have been liable to severe breakage. The cement filling and coating prevented both of these undesirable results.

(Although we are now considering what happened rather than why it happened, I hope you will not think of the appearance of cement at this time as being fore-ordained or somehow providential. Think of this in another way: if cement had not happened to appear, the change in height of crown and hence in diet would not have occurred. Animals tending in this direction but not developing cement would simply have died out. In some animals, cement happened to appear much earlier than in horses, and the other changes also occurred then. In other groups of plant-feeders, cement never happened to develop, and the change in diet never occurred.)

Once the new type of complicated, high-crowned, cement-covered grinding teeth was developed, no other really important changes occurred in the horse dentition. Evolution of the teeth slowed down markedly, and most of the minor changes that did occur seem to have little or no adaptive significance. After *Merychippus*, crowns did tend to become still higher for a time, but the change was not rapid; it fluctuated in different lines, and it was not carried to an extreme. *Equus* has very high crowns, but the height has a definite limit, not much exceeding three times the length (fore-and-aft) of the tooth. The highest crowns were developed not in *Equus* but in some of the extinct side-branches of the family. Among the latest forms of the little *Nannippus,* for instance, the height may be well over four times the length, but even in these the teeth did form closed roots and wear out eventually. These animals must have been unusually long-lived for their size, or else their teeth were higher-crowned than they really needed to be.

Some of the later grazing horses had the crown patterns somewhat more complicated than was usual in *Merychippus,* the ancestor of all of them, and some had the patterns somewhat simpler. Details of the pattern are highly variable in all those groups. Even features that were fairly constant in some groups and that can be used to distinguish the various genera and species do not, as a rule, seem to have any particular correlation with diet or advantage in one sort or another of environment. They look as if they had arisen more or less at random within the basic grazing type, the development of which in *Parahippus—Merychippus* clearly was not random.

24

HOW HORSES CHANGED:
LIMBS AND FEET

WILD or domestic, a horse is a runner. Speed is one of the essential elements in the horse's way of life. To a wild horse, speed often means life itself, for it is the main defense against hungry carnivores. This has apparently always been true; eohippus was already a fast animal and must have depended on flight to about as great an extent as does *Equus*. Unfortunately there is no way of clocking an eohippus or of matching it against *Equus*. It does, however, seem likely that eohippus was nearly as fast as the average wild Equidae now living. The proportions of eohippus and its whole running mechanism were similar to those of a medium-sized, fast dog of today, and such a dog, although no real match for a Thoroughbred, can often keep up with an average horse for short distances at least. (Fig. 29) It is claimed that coyotes have been timed at well over 40 miles per hour, rates better than the best horse racing records. Some question may exist as to this claim for the coyote, but there seems no doubt that dogs generally similar to eohippus in size and build can sprint at 35 miles per hour more or less, and that is fast for *Equus*.

Although some lines of horse evolution seem to show moderate increase in speed, the chances are that *Equus* is not much faster than was eohippus. Among the extinct horses there are some relatively heavy-bodied and short-legged forms that were probably slower runners than their ancestor, eohippus. Evidently the story of evolution in the horse limbs is not a simple one of increase in the efficiency

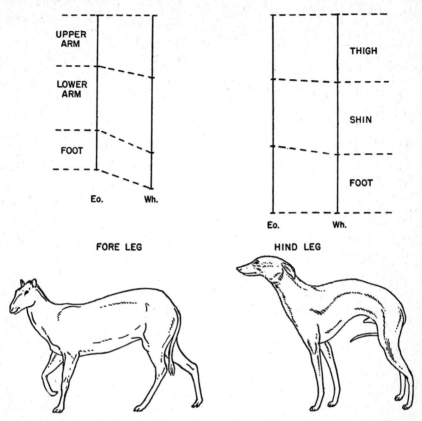

29. Comparison of eohippus (left) and a modern whippet (right). In the diagram above, the subdivisions of the lines are scaled to the actual lengths of bones in the various leg segments of each animal. Proportions are similar in the two, but eohippus has the front legs relatively shorter, hind legs relatively longer, and also has the lower leg segments slightly longer relative to the upper segments. Both sorts of differences in proportions are frequently associated with greater speed.

and performance of the running mechanism. Eohippus was already an efficient and speedy animal. It must again be emphasized that eohippus was not simply a small, imperfect *Equus*. It was an animal evidently as well adapted to its general way of life as *Equus* is—but it was a different sort of animal with a different way of life.

It is easy to infer one of the reasons why horses' legs and feet did change even though in eohippus they were already fast and efficient. Although increase in size has been quite irregular in horse history, it did occur at one time or another in most lines of descent. Now, if a 4-hand eohippus were simply enlarged to 16-hands, retaining all its proportions and structures, such a creature would be mechanically unsound. It certainly could not run as fast as a real eohippus, and it probably could not run at all, or would break its legs on the first gallop. Enlarging an animal to four times its original height, without change of proportions, means making it, not four, but *sixty-four* times as heavy (the cube of four, because it is cubic volume that determines weight). The absolute strength of bones and muscles would increase *sixteen* times. (Their strength depends on the area of the cross-section, and when diameter increases four times, area increases four-squared or sixteen times.) In other words, the bones and muscles of the enlarged animal would be only one-fourth as strong in relation to the weight they have to carry, and we can be quite sure that this would not be strong enough.

When horses became larger, their proportions had to change and their running mechanism had to become different, stronger, and more effective if they were to maintain the *same* speed as their smaller ancestors. This peculiar fact may remind you of Alice's experience when she had to run as fast as she could in order to stay in the same place.

(Perhaps you have marveled at the fact that a flea can jump about two hundred times its own length, and some writers have supposed that a flea as big as a man could therefore jump some 1,200 feet! Of course this is not true, for the same reasons that an eohippus as big as a race horse could not run as fast, or at all. A flea as big as a man could not jump one foot; it would simply collapse under its own weight.)

Mainly in response to this need, although other factors were evidently also involved, horse limbs and feet did change radically in the course of evolution in the family Equidae. Of course all these changes were related to each other and the various characters, such as number of toes and length of limb bones, did not evolve independently. The whole leg is part of a co-ordinated mechanism, and mechanical necessity makes it evolve as a unit even though there may be independent tendencies for variation in its different parts.

The changes have been described in considerable detail as far as they relate to the various separate bones and also, but to somewhat less extent, in regard to the way the bones fit together and their proportions to each other. There has been surprisingly little study of the way the whole mechanism worked and of what these changes actually meant in terms of the whole animal. Earlier students were so much concerned with recognizing and naming different kinds of teeth and bones of horses and tracing their lines of descent that they tended to neglect the horses as living animals. In spite of the tremendous labors of students of the horse family, here is a field of research that has barely been scratched.

Fortunately, enough has been done to give some general idea of main lines of functional change in horse limbs and feet. Regarding the feet, the old idea of a steady, uninterrupted reduction in number of toes is, as has lately become clear, not only over-simplified but also essentially false. Eohippus had four functional toes on the front feet. This number was reduced to three and finally to one in some later horses. So much is true, but the reduction was not universal, or constant, and simply counting the toes gives hardly any idea of what was really going on in regard to the functioning foot in the living animals. The story of horse foot evolution is summarized in Figs. 30-33.

Relatively slow-moving animals, like bears or men, often set their heels and (if they are four-footed) their wrists on the ground when they walk. Most of the faster animals have increased the effective length of the leg where it counts most, at the lower end, because their heels and wrists are held well up off the ground and the weight falls at the ends of the long bones corresponding to those of the palm (metacarpal bones) and instep (metatarsals) of man. This had already happened in eohippus, in which the wrist (corresponding with the 'knee' of *Equus*) and the heel (corresponding with the hock) were permanently raised. Eohippus bore its weight on the ends of the four metacarpals of the forefoot (one of which survives as the shank in *Equus*) and the three metatarsals of the hindfoot (one of which is the cannon bone in *Equus*). Below the ends of these bones and between and behind the toes was a heavy, flexible but tough pad or cushion. As each foot took off for a stride, it rolled up from the

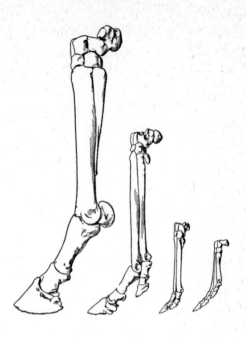

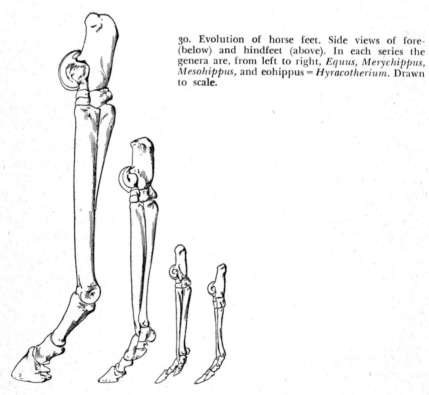

30. Evolution of horse feet. Side views of fore-
(below) and hindfeet (above). In each series the
genera are, from left to right, *Equus, Merychippus,
Mesohippus,* and eohippus = *Hyracotherium.* Drawn
to scale.

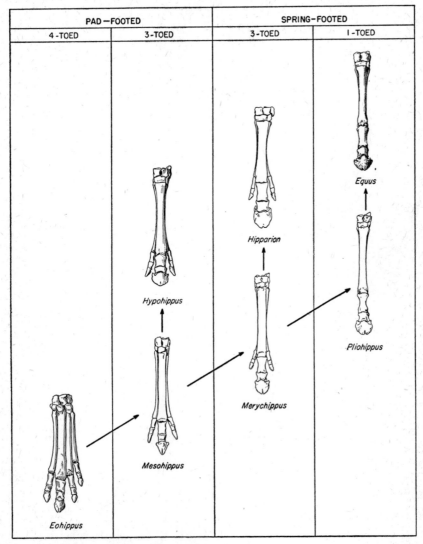

PAD—FOOTED		SPRING—FOOTED	
4-TOED	3-TOED	3-TOED	1-TOED

Equus

Hipparion

Hypohippus

Pliohippus

Merychippus

Mesohippus

Eohippus

31. Selected stages in the evolution of the forefoot of horses, oldest below. Each vertical column represents a distinctive mechanical type. Within each column (mechanical type) later forms do not show consistent tendencies toward reduction of side toes or other marked changes. Such changes occurred at definite times as shifts from one mechanical type to another. Drawn about same size, and not to scale, for comparison.

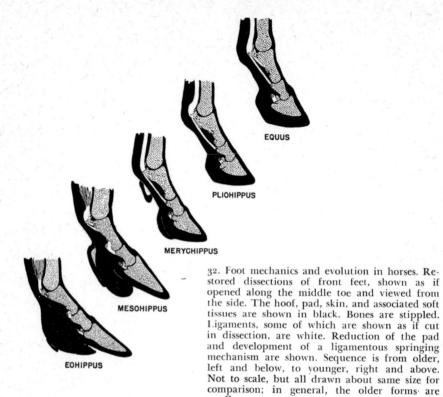

EQUUS

PLIOHIPPUS

MERYCHIPPUS

MESOHIPPUS

EOHIPPUS

32. Foot mechanics and evolution in horses. Restored dissections of front feet, shown as if opened along the middle toe and viewed from the side. The hoof, pad, skin, and associated soft tissues are shown in black. Bones are stippled. Ligaments, some of which are shown as if cut in dissection, are white. Reduction of the pad and development of a ligamentous springing mechanism are shown. Sequence is from older, left and below, to younger, right and above. Not to scale, but all drawn about same size for comparison; in general, the older forms are smaller.

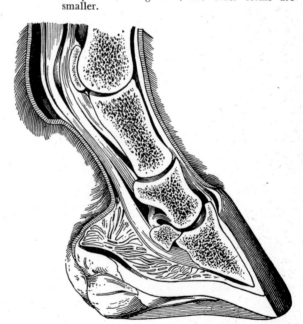

33. Vertical section of the toe of a recent horse, showing relationships of bones, ligaments, hoof, and other structures.

pad onto the toes and gave a final thrust from the small hooves on the ends of the toes. As the foot came down at the end of the stride, it landed on the cushion. You can see almost exactly how the mechanism worked by looking at the foot of the next friendly dog you chance to meet. The only obvious difference is that a dog has claws where eohippus had little hooves. In fact, except for not being hooked, even the hooves of eohippus were as much like a dog's claws as like the radically different hoof of *Equus*.

Throughout the Eocene, horses remained about the same size and their feet seem to have continued without any important structural change. In the Oligocene *Mesohippus* the only striking change was that one toe had been lost from the front foot. (There was still a vestige of it, but this had no remaining function.) Now both fore- and hindfeet were three-toed, as the hindfoot had already been in eohippus. It is not entirely clear why the change from four to three toes occurred at just this time, but it probably represented a mechanically stouter arrangement. It may be no coincidence that *Mesohippus* included the first horses to grow to sizes decidedly larger than eohippus. Three toes were adequate to carry the weight, and the heavier impact in these larger animals may have tended to cause injury to the more divergent fourth toe. The foot was still padded, as in eohippus, but the toes tended to be more compact, less spreading, and the main thrust of take-off in the stride apparently was derived more from the middle toes and not so evenly distributed over all the toes.

In the *Anchitherium—Hypohippus* line the feet seem to have changed relatively little from the Oligocene type, although they became stouter. It is evidence of how little attention has been paid to function, and not merely to form, in horse evolution that we do not know for sure whether the horses of this type still had padded feet, as in *Mesohippus,* or whether they had developed the new sort of mechanism seen in other three-toed horses and to be described in the next paragraph. It should be possible to determine this with reasonable probability, and I hope some student will soon be inspired to make this statement of our ignorance out of date.

In the other Miocene horses, by the time of *Merychippus* at least, a decided change had occurred in spite of the fact that these horses still had three functional toes on each foot as did *Mesohippus*. (More ignorance: we do not know just when this change arose in the *Mio-hippus—Parahippus—Merychippus* line.) There may still have been a vestige of the pad, but essentially the animal was now up permanently on extreme tiptoe, with the weight resting mainly or wholly on the hoof of the middle toe. This toe had stronger, more complex ligaments than in earlier horses, and the ligaments formed part of a spring mechanism. When the running animal landed on one foot, the middle toe was strongly flexed by the impact. This stretched the elastic ligaments. As the weight shifted forward and the foot came into position to take off on the next stride, the ligaments snapped back like rubber bands and literally bounced the animal forward. This spring makes for remarkably fast and efficient action in horses of increasing weight and is quite different from anything that can have occurred in earlier pad-footed types.

In *Merychippus* the side toes were still present and fully formed and each still ended in a well-developed hoof. In the resting position, however, the side hooves did not quite reach the ground, so that their function, if any, is rather puzzling. It has been commonly supposed that they had no function at this time and that this is a stage in their steady reduction, which was to culminate in the one-toed condition. Although this is stated or implied in almost every previous summary of horse evolution, it almost certainly is not true. Among the many descendants of *Merychippus* the *great majority* show *no* tendency for the small side toes to become still smaller. They fluctuated in size, of course, but by and large they remained at about the same relative length as in *Merychippus*. It looks as if in that genus they had reached the best length to perform some function and that they continued to perform that function in most later horses.

I think that this may be another case where we have gone astray because we have thought of extinct horses as skeletons standing stiffly in museum cases, and not as the mechanical frameworks of living animals. When you think what happens to a horse's foot in running, there is an entirely possible function for the short side toes, although I offer this here only as a hypothesis not yet sufficiently investigated. When a spring-footed horse is galloping and lands on the middle toe, this toe is bent upward far beyond its normal resting pose. At the point of extreme flexion, the short side toes of *Merychippus* and its later three-toed descendants *would* touch the ground. May they not, then, have had an essential function to act as buffers to stop the bending of the middle toe at this point and to lessen the danger of spraining the elastic ligaments by stretching them too far? They may also have had a subsidiary function to increase support when the animal was in soft ground and the middle toe sank in, but it is not probable that this alone could explain their retention and the lack of any definite further reduction in size in most horses.

By this time, we are accustomed to the idea—radical as it would have seemed to most of the earlier students—that the one-toed horses do not represent the outcome of a long and general tendency toward toe reduction in the horse family. They represented a new direction in horse evolution, a direction taken by only one of the numerous lines of descent among Pliocene horses.

Just what did happen here in modification of foot function? Not as much as might appear at first sight. In function, there is more difference between *Mesohippus* and *Merychippus,* both three-toed, than between three-toed *Merychippus* and one-toed *Equus.* The actual toe reduction took place in *Pliohippus,* and it occurred with remarkable rapidity as evolutionary changes go. The spring mechanism was retained and apparently still worked almost exactly as in *Merychippus.* It had become considerably stronger in these larger animals, and this tendency continued in the still larger descendants of *Pliohippus.*

Except for increase in strength, a necessity for springing with increasing weight, the only essential change was loss of the lateral buffers, if my guess is correct that this was the function of the side toes. Let us speculate a little further: If the buffer were not *necessary,* it would be *disadvantageous.* The slender side toes were undoubtedly liable to frequent injury. They would become unnecessary if the springing ligaments became stronger and less liable to sprain and if there were some other adequate means of checking the stretching of these ligaments. We know that the springing ligaments did become stronger, and we know that in *Equus* there are powerful check ligaments that guard against strain. If this speculation is on the right track, it is probable that the check ligaments were weaker, or possibly absent, in the horses with side-toe buffers. This point has not yet been adequately investigated.

In any case, the springing mechanism did reach its highest development in *Equus* and this is an essential factor in permitting these animals to reach such large size and still to retain great speed. Camp and Smith, whose research published in 1942 gave us our best insight into how fossil horse feet really worked, have described the *Equus* foot mechanism in these words: 'The action resembles that of a boy jumping on a pogo-stick; the harder the impact, the higher the bounce—up to the capacity of the apparatus.'

This 'capacity of the apparatus' is severely taxed in large modern horses. Lameness is distressingly frequent in domestic horses, and this is almost always caused by injury to the springing mechanism of the feet. The law of diminishing returns is taking over at the stage reached by *Equus*. The speed mechanism of modern horses can bear little more weight. Thanks to the perfection of this mechanism, they are about as fast as seems mechanically possible for animals of their size. They could become still larger only by becoming slower.

This retention of speed with increasing size and the limits on it are also reflected in other features of the evolution of legs in horses. It has long been recognized that swiftly running animals usually have the upper leg bones relatively short and the lower leg bones relatively long. The heavy leg muscles are mostly attached to the upper leg; the shorter these are the faster they can move. The whole leg moves more easily and rapidly if the main weight is in the upper not the lower parts. On the other hand, the longer the leg, the greater the stride and the more ground covered for each contraction of the muscles. It is, then, to be expected that for mechanical reasons fast animals should have long legs but with the length mainly in the lower leg bones. It is also to be expected that the muscles should be bunched in the upper leg and that their extensions into the lower leg should be tendinous rather than fleshy. This is not the whole story, as is evident from the comparison of pad versus spring foot, but these expectations usually do work out.

In very heavy animals there is an opposite tendency. They require exceptional power and long muscle leverage in order to support and move their bulk, and there is a corresponding tendency in them for the upper leg bones to be relatively long and the lower bones relatively short.

In the evolution of the horse, there was some tendency for changes in leg-bone proportions, with the upper leg bones becoming relatively shorter and the lower relatively longer. This was rather erratic, but it apparently was fairly general in middle stages of the family's history at any rate, and it is what would be expected if maintenance of speed was an essential part of that history. In the largest, late forms, however, including *Equus,* the tendency to change farther in this direction is no longer clear, and in some of these lines there may even be some apparent reversion, with the lower leg tending to become shorter relative to the upper. Here again, these animals have apparently reached the limit where the advantages of speed and of larger size conflict: they can become heavier only if they become slower.

Other changes that occurred in the leg bones seem to be related to need for increasing strength and for increasing rigidity in the joints. (Fig. 34) These features have an essential relationship to the specialized use of the legs for locomotion, with no other important function, and particularly to the limitation of lateral motion that must occur if constant dislocations are to be avoided in such increasingly bulky running, springing animals. Eohippus still had considerable flexibility in the legs, probably about as much as has a dog and rather less than a cat—or a man. You can turn your hand either back up or palm up without displacing your elbow, because there are two separate bones, radius and ulna, in the forearm and these can be twisted in a rotary movement. Your foot rotation is more limited, but some is still possible because of the two separate bones, tibia and fibula, in your shin. Eohippus still had these separate bones

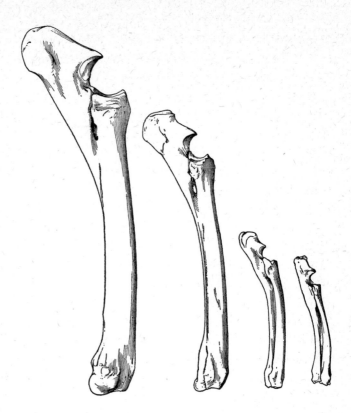

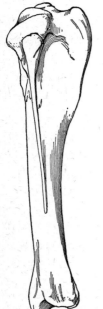

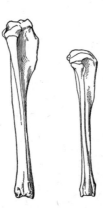

34. Evolution of bones of the forearm, above, and shin (gaskin), below, in horses. In each series the genera are, from left to right: *Equus, Merychippus, Mesohippus,* and eohippus = *Hyracotherium.* Drawn to scale.

in the forearm and shin ('gaskin' of *Equus*) and the leg joints permitted some freedom of movement.

In larger animals running on their toes and using the feet for nothing else, this freedom is not only unnecessary but also positively dangerous. (You know that this is so if you have ever turned your ankle.) In *Mesohippus* the motion was already sharply limited and this was increasingly true of later horses. In the forearm, radius and ulna fused tightly together and the shaft of the united bone was finally formed by the radius, stouter of the two formerly separate bones. In the gaskin, the tibia and fibula similarly fused and the smaller bone, the fibula, tended to become vestigial. Joints, except those at shoulder and hip, tended to become more pulley-like, restricting motion to one plane.

The whole picture of horse leg and foot evolution cannot be summed up as one broad trend from eohippus to *Equus*. It shows instead a series of rather sharply different stages within any one of the longer lines of descent, often with divergence among contemporaneous lines, and with considerable fluctuation throughout. The most nearly continuous features seem to be mechanically correlated with increase in size, when this occurred, but even here the response to needs imposed by greater weight may be quite different in different cases. Some of the major features may be summarized as follows:

1. Eocene horses, small in size, had light, fast limbs, still rather flexible, with pad-feet and with four toes on each forefoot and three on each hindfoot.

2. At the beginning of the Oligocene there was a change, probably rather rapid (there is a gap in our knowledge here), to three-toed feet, both fore and hind, with increasing emphasis on the middle toe, but the weight still rested on a pad. Limb motion was becoming restricted to the fore-and-aft plane.

3. In the Miocene there was a split into two or more lines with different foot types. One, inadequately studied, apparently retained feet somewhat like those of Oligocene horses but increasingly stout and perhaps tapir- or even rhinoceros-like (*Anchitherium* and its allies).

4. Another Miocene line, that running through *Merychippus,* developed a mechanism for springing from the third toe. The side toes were retained but did not touch the ground when the animal was at rest. They probably served as buffers for the springing mechanism.

5. Most Pliocene horses retained essentially the foot mechanism of *Merychippus* with variations either random or correlated with the sizes of the animals.

6. One Pliocene line, through *Pliohippus,* retained the spring mechanism of *Merychippus* but rapidly lost the side-toe buffers while the spring ligaments became progressively both simpler and stronger, and effective check ligaments occurred. This line terminates in the modern horse, in which possibilities for increase of size and for maintenance or increase of speed have reached an extreme and may begin to conflict.

The beginning and end of the whole complex story appear in a comparison of two great runners: little eohippus and big *Equus* (Plate XXXIIb).

25

PATTERNS OF EVOLUTION

FROM the start of this discussion, it has been kept in mind that the evolution of the horse family, interesting in itself, also teaches lessons of broader value. Even if we did not particularly care how horses have evolved, we should still be intensely concerned with how evolution operates as a general principle. Evolution is the process that has produced mankind, along with all other living things. The more we understand about the process, the better we shall understand ourselves and the world we live in. Knowledge of horse evolution, although not complete (what field of human knowledge is wholly complete?), is already so good that it is one of our best means of determining how evolution works. No other animals have undergone precisely the same changes in skull, teeth, feet, or other parts, but the ways in which these changes occur, the broad patterns of evolution, have essential similarities in all groups.

One of the greatest and most disputed problems about the general pattern of evolution has been labeled *orthogenesis*. The term was coined from two Greek words meaning 'straight' and 'origin' or 'development.' The idea back of it is the belief or theory that evolution usually (some students would say 'always') operates in straight lines. Once a sort of evolutionary change has started, the doctrine of orthogenesis claims that it will tend to keep on indefinitely. If, for instance, evolving animals start increasing in size, it is supposed that the increase will continue constantly and steadily until the animals finally become extinct. If this is so, then it would appear that evolution tends to follow some sort of established plan or that it is ruled by some inner life force aside from random change or fluctuat-

ing living conditions. In this way, observation of how evolution occurs clearly has an important bearing on the ultimate problems of
why it occurs.

Here the evidence of the horse family is of crucial importance, as
has been recognized by practically everyone who has ever discussed
this important question. Earlier students usually pointed to the evolution of the horse as a typical example of orthogenesis and the best
proof of that theory. It is now seen that this was a serious mistake,
a mistake caused in part by inadequate evidence and in still larger
part by superficial and erroneous methods of study. Some students
of evolution who were not really well acquainted with the whole
picture of horse evolution simply picked out parts of it that seemed
to fit an orthogenetic interpretation, and their false conclusions were
accepted and endlessly repeated by others who knew still less about
the subject.

The evolution of the horse family was definitely not orthogenetic.
The preceding chapters have made this abundantly clear. There was,
for instance, no constant and over-all increase in size. Most recent
horses are larger than most ancient horses, but when the history is
examined in detail it shows that there have been long periods when
no increase in size occurred and also several branches of horse evolution in which the animals became markedly smaller, not larger.
The feet did not steadily change from four toes to three and then to
one. In the last chapter it was shown that foot evolution followed
different lines in different branches of the family and that toe reduction, for instance, from three to one was not a continuation of a
previous trend, an orthogenetic process, but was a change in evolutionary direction, a new development that occurred at just one time
and in only one group of horses. And so it goes for all the changes
that have occurred in the history of the family; not one of them
shows the constant, guided change in a single direction that is demanded by the theory of orthogenesis. In reality, the horse family
goes far to disprove that theory, and when other supposed examples
of orthogenesis are examined with similar care they, too, are found
to be opposed to the reality of orthogenesis in any strict sense.

On the other hand, horse evolution has not taken place wholly at random. There is more to the history than change according to chance alone. The rather rapid changes in the teeth, for instance, from *Parahippus* through *Merychippus* to its immediate successors proceeded in a systematic way, fluctuating always but tending toward the same result: high, cement-covered teeth with complex enamel folds. There was some guiding or orienting influence at work here. But when we examine variations in the teeth of *Merychippus* and the differences between descendants of *Merychippus* such as *Hipparion* and *Pliohippus,* there is evidently something random involved here also. The teeth became systematically higher and systematically developed grinding enamel crests, but there is nothing systematic about some details in the precise pattern of those crests. Certain elements in the pattern fluctuated greatly, and it seems to be pure chance that *Hipparion* inherited one sort of pattern and *Pliohippus* another sort.

The evidence of the horses thus indicates that evolution is not strictly oriented or guided and not strictly random, but that it is a mixture of the two. Some characteristics evolve in a regular and systematic way while others evolve erratically and as if by chance. This is apparently true of all evolution, and it is one of the great and basic discoveries regarding the *how* of evolution.

Another step forward in the understanding of this process is made when we note that the degree of orientation or of randomness in evolution depends in most cases and perhaps in all on the functional nature of the characteristics involved. The more important or essential a characteristic is for the way of life of the animal involved, the more systematic is its evolution. The less important the characteristic may be in its functional aspects, the more fluctuation and randomness it shows in its history. In the example of the horse teeth in *Merychippus* and its immediate successors, these horses were becoming strictly grazing animals. It was important for them, in fact essential for success in this new way of life, that the teeth become high-crowned, cement-covered, and complexly ridged. The precise pattern of the ridges made relatively little difference. A molar tooth can grind about as well whether the protocone is attached to the protoconule or protoselene, as in *Pliohippus,* or not, as in *Hipparion.*

An evolutionary trend that continues or intensifies a characteristic already incipient, such as increasing height of tooth crowns in these horses, represents oriented and usually straight-line (but not, in a technical sense, orthogenetic) evolution. It normally involves the intensification or perfection of an existing functional relationship; in the example, the function involved is that of grazing, or grass-eating. Another example in the horse family was the development of the three-toed, springing foot with side-toe buffers. Such evolution normally stops when the function is adequately fulfilled. (This is further evidence that the process is not really orthogenetic.) It may, however, be continued or reactivated if some other development, such as increase in size, makes the functioning inadequate again and requires further or different mechanical adjustment.

Besides this sort of *trend* evolution, evolution in general and that of the horse family in particular often display a related but distinct directional process, that of *transformation*. A trend involves the continuation of an existing direction of change, while a transformation involves a change in evolutionary direction, the rise of a new sort of functional relationship. In horses, the change from pad-foot to spring-foot and the change from browsing teeth to grazing teeth were transformations. More profound transformations are relatively uncommon in evolution, but have great importance when they do occur. The change of a fish fin into a foot and, much later, the change of a reptile foot into a bird's wing were transformations of most far-reaching significance. So, still later, were the various transformations involved in our own history, such as changes that arose when our four-footed ancestors reared up and became two-footed.

Both trends and transformations commonly lead to increased *specialization*. This evolutionary concept is rather vague and is difficult to define in a really clear-cut way. Every living thing has certain requirements and limitations that confine it to a definite place in nature and that restrict its immediate possibilities for further evolution. Most fishes must live in water, and the great majority of them must live either in salt water or in fresh water and cannot change at will from one to the other. Most reptiles must live on land, and the majority of them can live only in certain places on land, places, for instance, that do not have too cold a year-round climate and that provide certain types of food. Every animal and plant has such special requirements; none can live literally anywhere on earth and in this sense all are specialized.

There are, however, different degrees of specialization. Requirements may be broader or narrower. Bears, or men, can live on a great variety of foods. In this respect, their specialization is slight, or is relatively broad. Other animals are highly specialized in food habits: weasels must have fresh blood and meat; koalas (the quaint Australian 'teddy-bears') can live only on the leaves of one sort of tree. Recent horses must have grass in order to survive, and they are relatively specialized in food habits. Eohippus could not eat grass, but it could probably eat a wider variety of other plant foods and so was, on the whole, less specialized. The pad-foot of eohippus, borne by a leg still somewhat flexible, was also capable of a rather wider variety of functional relationships than is the rigid limb and spring-foot of *Equus* and other late horses. There was thus some narrowing of functions in the evolution of the horse, and to this extent some increase in specialization. Its extent was not, however, very great within the horse family. Eohippus was already a relatively specialized sort of animal. As regards the horses, change in sort of specialization is more striking than increase in its degree.

Although increase in specialization, in the sense of limitation of functional possibilities and required environmental conditions, is common in evolution, it is not universal. In the evolution of man, specialization in this particular sense of the word has decreased rather than increased. It seems obvious that man has a much wider scope of activities and can occupy a far wider range of environments than could his primate ancestors. This is one of the essential features of human evolution, and one that distinguishes it from the more usual sequences like that in the horse family.

In another sense, specialization may be considered as a decrease in the possibilities for further evolutionary change. The feet of eohippus, for example, obviously could evolve in a variety of ways, into later three-toed pad-feet, into three-toed spring-feet, and into one-toed spring-feet, as actually occurred in different lines. Other possibilities existed, although they did not happen to arise. The one-toed spring-foot of *Equus* and other descendants of *Pliohippus* seems to have evolved as far as it can, and the origin of any different sort of foot from this, although not quite impossible, is certainly extremely improbable. If changing conditions were to make the *Equus* type of foot disadvantageous, it is more likely that horses would become extinct than that they would or could develop a new sort of foot to meet the changing needs.

In general, more specialized animals are more liable to extinction both because they have more special requirements for living and because their possibilities for change are fewer. This is the basis for the principle of the *survival of the less-specialized,* sometimes called 'Cope's law' (after the great paleontologist, E. D. Cope, who has been mentioned on a previous page). Like many other 'laws' of evolution, this simply describes what has often happened and is not a hard and fast rule of nature. That 'Cope's law' has not had invariable force in evolution is clear from the fact that it does not apply to the horse family. The surviving horse is actually one of the most specialized members of the family, and more primitive forms are all extinct. Specialization may open opportunities for further evolution rather than restricting them, and often we can judge only by the results. Our ancestors lost evolutionary possibilities, such as the possibility of becoming as fleet as horses, when they ceased to walk on all fours, and yet this specialization gained them new possibilities that far more than repaid the loss.

Even when specialization has really restricted total possibilities for further change, as seems to be true of the modern horse, it is more likely to be advantageous than disadvantageous unless a marked change in environmental conditions occurs. This explains why many highly specialized types have survived, as has the horse. When, however, such changes do occur, the survival of the less-specialized becomes the rule. For instance the living opossums of North and South America are very ancient, relatively little-specialized mammals. In South America they had numerous more specialized relatives during the Age of Mammals, almost all of which have become extinct while the opossum still thrives.

This question of specialization also bears on another evolutionary principle, that of the *irreversibility of evolution,* often called 'Dollo's Law' (after Louis Dollo, a famous Belgian paleontologist). This states that an evolving group of animals does not return to the condition of its ancestors. Recent study has established that this law, too, is not absolute but is only a description of what is usual in evolution. Return to ancestral structure is not flatly impossible, it is merely improbable. If the ancestral condition is very remote and the changes great, the improbability is enormous and approaches impossibility. It is practically impossible that an animal just like eohippus should evolve from *Equus* and extremely improbable (but not impossible) that one-toed *Equus* should give rise to any normally three-toed descendants. When the change is not so great or when it involves only one or two simple characteristics, reversibility is not particularly improbable. We have seen, for instance, that there was nothing improbable in reversing the trend for horses to become larger; the reversion did several times occur. Reversion is particularly improbable when it would involve regaining some structure that has been lost, such as the side toes of the horse or, as a more far-reaching example, the gills of the fishes that were ancestral to all reptiles and mammals.

Traces of the ancient side toes still occur in horse embryos, and traces of gills still occur in all mammal embryos, including both horses and men. This sort of thing is the basis for the *principle of recapitulation,* sometimes called the 'biogenetic law.' In its original form, as put forward by earlier students of evolution in the past century, this principle claimed that each developing organism goes through stages representing the successive steps in its ancestry. In that form, the principle simply is not true. Horses and men develop gill-like slits at an early stage in their embryological development not because this represents the adult stage of fishes in their remote ancestry, but because they have inherited a system of development in which such slits occur. The slits appear at corresponding stages in the embryos of fish and of horses, but thereafter they develop quite differently in the two. Some features of fish development have been lost altogether, some have been strongly modified, and many wholly new features have been added.

Animals have to live and to be well adapted throughout their whole development, and not merely when they are adults. Many characters of the embryo and of the young are specially evolved adaptations for those stages and reveal nothing about ancestral adults. The fact that a colt, for instance, has relatively long, slender legs does not mean that adult ancestors of *Equus* had longer legs than the modern horse. A colt needs long legs to survive, in order to be able to reach its standing mother to nurse and in order to be more nearly able to keep up with her in flight. Although recapitulation thus fails to provide the clear guide to ancestry that was claimed by its early advocates, it does add to the evidence. The fact that fishes and horses have similarities in their early embryological development is good evidence that they are distantly related, even though the horse embryo does not really go through a stage representative of an ancestral fish.

Among the many other general evolutionary principles well illustrated by the horse family are those of divergence, adaptive radiation, parallelism, and convergence.

Divergence in evolution means just what it sounds like, that different lines of descent from one ancestral group tend to diverge, to follow different paths of evolution, and to become specialized to different degrees and in different ways. We have seen this happening repeatedly in horse history. It occurred as early as the Eocene among European descendants of eohippus or *Hyracotherium* (see chapter 19). It happened in America among the early Miocene horses and again, to even more striking degree, in the late Miocene and early Pliocene (see chapters 15 and 17). A result was that all at one time, in the Pliocene, there were three-toed browsing horses, three-toed grazing horses, and one-toed grazing horses, and several different sorts of each.

One of the results of such divergence, which occurs on a smaller or larger scale at one time or another in the histories of most groups of animals, is *adaptive radiation*. Different lines of descent diverge or radiate so that they come to have quite distinct adaptive relationships or ways of life, to play different available roles in the economy of life. The three main types of Pliocene horses just mentioned did this, and they represent an adaptive radiation within the horse family. On a broader scale, the whole horse family itself represents one branch of an earlier (early Paleocene) and greater adaptive radiation that produced a great variety of carnivorous and herbivorous mammals. On a scale grander still, the whole class of mammals has undergone complex adaptive radiation into such radically distinct types as moles, bats, rabbits, beavers, whales, horses, and men, to mention only a few among the multitude.

It sometimes happens that different lines of descent, instead of diverging and coming to follow different ways of life, evolve in such a way as to follow much the same ways. If their ancestors were the same or rather similar to start with, this is called *parallel evolution,* and if the ancestors were distinctly different from each other it is called *convergent evolution.* (The difference is not always particularly clear or important.) This does not happen if the two groups in question live together and are or become so similar that they compete with each other. In such competition one line is sure to be nipped in the bud and not to continue long in parallel evolution or to become really closely like the other in convergent evolution.

Parallel and convergent evolution between two groups of animals occurs only when the groups happen to take up similar ways of life and corresponding adaptive sorts of evolution, at different times or in different places, or both. A striking case of parallel evolution is provided by *Plagiolophus* (see chapter 19), which achieved by the end of the Eocene adaptive characteristics very like those of *Merychippus* in the late Miocene. Both groups were derived from eohippus (or something quite like it) and their evolution was closely parallel, but this development occurred earlier and more rapidly in *Plagiolophus.* Equally striking examples of convergence toward the true horses are provided by the South American notohippids and proterotheres (see chapter 20). Although their ancestry was decidedly different from that of the horses, these animals adopted horse-like ways of life and became in various respects closely similar to horses. They were geographically isolated from the horses and did not come into competition with these because they lived in South America while it was an island continent and before horses reached there.

These processes of parallel and convergent evolution often produce striking resemblances among different groups of animals, but they never produce complete identity. Even in closely parallel descent from the same ancestry, identity is lost because of the random effects in evolution and because the conditions to which they are adapting are never precisely the same in two different regions or at two different times. In cases of convergence, the distinctions usually remain still clearer, because there are ancestral differences that are not wholly wiped out by later and usually more superficial adaptation to similar ways of life.

These same examples of parallelism and convergence also illustrate striking differences in rate of evolution. *Plagiolophus* and the noto-hippids developed high, cement-covered teeth at faster rates than did the true horses. One of the proterotheres was already in the Miocene more completely one-toed than the horses are now. Even within the horse family, different characters evolved at markedly different rates at different times and in different lines. Evolution in size and in limbs and feet was practically nil during millions of years in the Eocene, but relatively rapid in some lines at later times. In the Miocene, evolution of the teeth was almost completely static in some groups of horses and exceptionally rapid in some others. These and many similar facts clearly show that there is no constant, over-all force pushing evolution along. If there is any general ordained *plan* of evolution, it must be insanely erratic. Here again we touch on evidence of the greatest importance for deciding *why* evolution occurs.

A point of almost equally broad importance and one that has been much discussed by students of evolution involves the question whether evolution usually, or always, proceeds by the accumulation of numerous, small changes, or whether it sometimes, or commonly, produces a distinctly new sort of animal all at once. For the horse family, at least, this question is answered. Apart from one or two small gaps in our knowledge, all of horse evolution is clearly shown to have proceeded by many small steps, not by a few large jumps or *saltations*. Horse evolution was a continuous process in the sense that each successive population grades into or overlaps the last, with merely a shift in the average condition or in the extreme variants in the direction of the evolution that is occurring. This is true even of rather radical changes which did occur at relatively rapid rates, such as the loss of the (external) side toes in *Pliohippus*. We never find a new structural norm or a new genus appearing all at once, but only by intergradation in the populations when the evidence is sufficient. *Parahippus* and *Merychippus*, for instance, are strikingly different if we compare early *Parahippus* and late *Merychippus*, but when early *Merychippus* arose from late *Parahippus*, the intergradation is so perfect that it becomes merely arbitrary which name should be applied to a given specimen.

The possibility of occasional saltation in evolution is not completely ruled out, but the horses show that very radical changes, as between eohippus and *Equus*, for instance, may occur without saltation and, along with much other evidence, strongly suggest that saltation is not a usual and probably not an important evolutionary event.

The horses seem to give us a good, typical picture of major evolutionary processes. It is not, however, to be assumed that they illustrate all such processes and that evolution of all animals has always proceeded as in the horses. The same forces were doubtless always involved, but they might work out rather differently in different sorts of animals and under different conditions. The horses have, for instance, been abundant animals throughout their history and apparently had quite large interbreeding populations. There is some reason to believe that the same evolutionary forces would produce different results in rare animals with very small local populations. The random effects in evolution would, for example, probably be more potent and striking in such a group than they are in horse evolution, where, nevertheless, they do also occur.

In the complete picture of horse evolution, and probably in that of the evolution of any group of animals, there seem to be three different sorts of patterns or kinds of events, often going on simultaneously, and most intricately interwoven, and yet distinguishable on close analysis. There is, first, splitting, the division of one group of animals into two or more. On a large scale, this is, or may lead to, divergence and adaptive radiation. On a smaller scale, it is the process usually called *speciation*. Then there is evolution going on in a continuous line of ancestors and descendants. Later members of such a line are often quite different from the earlier members. This commonly occurs even though there has been no splitting of the line into several different groups, although, of course, such splitting usually goes on at the same time. These changes by descent, regardless of splitting or speciation, most frequently involve rather slow adjustment to gradually changing conditions or increasing specialization for given conditions. This part of evolution is sometimes called *phyletic evolution*. Finally this change by descent may involve relatively rapid (but apparently seldom or never instantaneous) shift to a new adaptive type, the acquisition of a more or less radically distinct way of life. Some students call this sort of change *quantum evolution*.

The rates of speciation and of phyletic evolution vary greatly at different times and in different groups. One or the other, or both, may slow down or even stop in occasional phases of evolution. It is, however, usual for both to be going on at the same time and rather continuously in the history of any group of animals. Quantum evolution, on a small scale, may occur quite frequently in the history of a given group, but even so it is essentially intermittent. The 'quantum' shift to any new type takes place in a relatively circumscribed part of the history and then is followed by more continuous phyletic evolution within the new type. Larger quantum shifts, involving more radical changes in adaptive relationships, are relatively rare, but are, of course, of great importance when they do occur. All three modes of evolution have occurred among horses, and examples of them may be found in preceding pages.

The existence at the present time of (at least) six distinct species of living *Equus* (true horses: *E. caballus;* onagers: *E. hemionus;* true asses: *E. asinus;* and three species of zebras: *E. quagga, E. zebra,* and *E. grevyi*) is an example of the results of speciation. Sometime in the past, around the beginning of the Pleistocene, the ancestors of these species all belonged to a single, variable, interbreeding group. This group spread widely over Asia, Europe, and Africa, and as it did so, the different local populations changed in somewhat different ways. Eventually some of these populations ceased to interbreed with each other and then they developed more constant and distinctive differences and became separate species. Among the more widespread species, such as *Equus quagga* (see chapter 4), the local groups tend to differ considerably among themselves, even though there is still some interbreeding among them. If this interbreeding were to stop permanently between any two parts of the population of the whole species, it would result in splitting into two distinct species. In speciation, this is the crucial point: the stopping of interbreeding. Anything that has this result is called an *isolating mechanism*. There is a great variety of isolating mechanisms, but the one most often effective as the beginning of the process of speciation is simply geographic separation of the two (or more) groups. Sooner or later, if the separation persists, this is reinforced and made irrevocable by the development (in a variety of ways) of some sort of genetical incompatibility. The heredity mechanisms of the separate groups become different in a way that prevents their producing fertile offspring, or any offspring at all, even if they should come in contact.

Each of the numerous lines of descent in the Equidae from Eocene to Recent is a good example of phyletic evolution. The process has already been rather fully discussed in preceding chapters. The line from eohippus to *Hypohippus,* for example (see chapters 13-15), exemplifies fairly continuous phyletic evolution. (Of course, speciation was going on all the time in these groups too, even though it has not been specially discussed in this more general treatment.)

Quantum evolution of a major sort does not occur within the Equidae. Even the most contrasting members of the family all belong to the same general and broad adaptive type. There are, however, a number of lesser changes in type involved in the family history. Those of the most minor sort merely demonstrate that quantum evolution and phyletic evolution intergrade and are not absolutely distinct parts of what is, over-all, one great evolutionary process. Some other adaptive shifts can be more distinctly recognized as involving quantum evolution. The change from browsing to grazing (see chapter 23) is probably the best example.

26

EXPLANATIONS OF EVOLUTION

WHAT? How? Why? These are the three great questions for any investigation. Some features of the 'what' and 'how' of horse evolution have been summarized in chapters 22-5. Now we are coming to the end of our inquiry and the time has come to face the final question: Why? Every student of evolution has tried to find some sort of answer, even if only a partial answer, to this fundamental problem—and these students include many thousands of learned men over a period of two centuries or more.

Of course the earliest students knew little about the 'what' and less about the 'how' of evolution, so that their suggestions about 'why' were sometimes merely wild speculations. This was especially true of most of the pre-Darwinian students. Even after Darwin's *Origin of Species* (first published in 1859, as has been mentioned earlier), there have been some who produced theories that were almost pure fantasy, instead of taking the trouble to base their ideas painstakingly on established facts and to check them by observations and experiments. I suppose there always will be such mentally undisciplined characters, even within the fold of science, but we need not pay much serious attention to them.

More sober students during the first fifty or sixty years after *The Origin of Species* made a series of attempts to explain evolution and produced a number of different, although seldom completely conflicting, explanations. As we reconsider these now in the light of tremendously increased and still rapidly increasing knowledge of 'what' and 'how,' most of them have made a real and distinct contribution toward an understanding of evolution. They were, however, merely partial explanations, at best. Usually they tried to boil down the causes of evolution to one rather simple explanation, and it has now become abundantly clear that evolution is an exceedingly complex process that involves the interaction of a wide variety of factors. Usually, too, they went astray at some point—even Darwin did—and produced theories that were, if partly true, also partly false beyond much present doubt.

Finally, today, a majority of students of the subject agree on the major and most essential features of a general theory of evolution, which rests on a synthesis of facts and of theories derived from innumerable studies in all the different fields of the life sciences. Perhaps the simplest way toward a summary of the origin and nature of this modern theory is to review briefly the essential features of some of the earlier theories that have, in one way or another, contributed to advancing comprehension.

One of the older speculations about evolution was that it is caused, in the main at least, by the adaptive relationship between organisms and their environment. We all know that individual plants and animals can be markedly altered by the conditions in which they live and by their own activities. A seed planted in poor soil produces a spindly plant and an exactly similar seed in good soil produces a luxurious plant quite different in appearance. The 'before' and 'after' pictures in advertisements are believable at least to the extent that exercises, steam baths, drugs, and other things can produce visible changes in our bodies. Before Darwin, Buffon speculated that evolution might result from action of the environment on organisms, and Lamarck speculated that evolution might involve, among other things, the effects of use and disuse of organs in accordance with the habitual reactions of organisms to their environments.

After Darwin, these ideas were revived, combined, and systematized in a theory usually called 'neo-Lamarckian,' although it was in some respects quite different from Lamarck's own ideas on the subject. The essential point of the neo-Lamarckian theory was that modifications acquired by a plant or animal during its lifetime would to some degree affect its offspring in the same way and that this would eventually produce evolutionary change. The trouble with this theory, as has finally been clearly established, is that such modifi-cations do *not* affect the offspring in the same way and cannot really become hereditary. Thus (in spite of certain minor exceptions in particular circumstances) no such change can lead to evolution, the basic characteristic of which is precisely change in heredity.

The theory had a great appeal and seemed to be backed by exten-sive evidence because of the fact that all organisms are intricately adapted structurally to their own activities and to their environ-ments. This is a fact, and the neo-Lamarckians were also essentially right in concluding that this adaptation is a main element in orient-ing evolution, in determining the direction in which change usually occurs. But they had the cart before the horse. Adaptation does not cause evolution. Evolution causes adaptation, that is, adaptation is not a basic factor but is the result of the interaction of a whole com-plex of other evolutionary processes. It is also evident that the theory, even if it had been true, could not have been complete. We have seen even in the usually adaptive evolution of the horses that non-adaptive change also occurs, and neo-Lamarckians had no ex-planation for this.

Another part of Lamarck's theory was the idea that living things have an inherent tendency to evolve, that their changes tend to follow some sort of ordained plan regardless of any merely material interactions of organism and environment. This idea was repudiated by the neo-Lamarckians, but variations on it were frequently ad-vanced by later students. The belief that evolution is produced or guided by some property or principle peculiar to life is called *vital-ism,* and there have been many different, often conflicting, proposals of vitalistic theories of evolution. Many of these have also involved *finalism,* the idea that evolution has proceeded toward a goal and that changes arise because they are in the direction with that goal.

Discussion of these ideas would lead us far astray into the laby-rinthine paths of philosophy, but it may be pointed out that they have two main and crippling faults from a strictly scientific point of view: they do not really fit the facts, and even if they did, they would still fail to explain those facts. In order to fit these theories, evolution would have to be orthogenetic (see chapter 25). The theories have, in fact, almost always been supported by the claim that evolution really is orthogenetic. But we have seen on the evidence of the horse family (and much other evidence agrees) that this simply is not true: evolution is *not* orthogenetic in the sense required by vitalism or, especially, finalism.

If the vitalist says that evolution is something inherent in life, well, perhaps that is true in the sense that life does have the property of evolving; and yet the statement does not explain evolution and, when you get right down to it, really does not mean anything. It is as non-explanatory and as meaningless as saying that heat is inherent in fire. Such a statement does not in the least advance our knowledge of what heat is, or what fire is, or what is going on in a flame. Similarly the vitalist theories have made no real contribution to understanding life or evolution. Yet they are, even now, sometimes advanced with an air of profundity by philosophers (especially amateur philosophers) ignorant of most of the facts of evolution. It has seemed advisable to include this brief mention of them, so that you may not be taken in by their pretensions; but they do not help us toward an explanation.

To return to more fruitful earlier theories, that of Darwin was much the most important of these and has contributed the most to the modern theory, even though this is no longer strictly Darwinian. The most important feature of Darwin's theory, and the most important single contribution ever made to the understanding of evolution, was the idea of selection, especially natural selection. Plants and animals always vary, even within a single species. This variation is in part a result of differences in their heredity. Some variations are advantageous and some are disadvantageous. On the whole, the organisms with advantageous variations are fitter and on an average more of them will survive, while more of those with disadvantageous variations will die before they reproduce. Therefore, the fitter animals will pass on more of their heredity to the next generation and evolutionary change will tend to occur in the direction of increasing fitness, or adaptation.

This principle is certainly true, and it constitutes one of the most important elements in any modern explanation of evolution. Nevertheless, Darwin's theory still had some serious imperfections that prevented its being accepted by many students of evolution. The theory explained why unfit or inadaptive types of organisms tend to be eliminated, but it did not seem adequately to explain the much more important origin of more fit, better adapted organisms. It also failed to explain why evolution is not completely adaptive—why different types of organisms may evolve even though their relationships with the environment seem to be exactly the same, why adaptation is seldom or never perfect, and why non-adaptive characters (those not involved in adaptation) and inadaptive characters (those opposed to harmonious adaptation) do often arise in evolution. These features of evolution were not well explained by the older forms of Darwinian theory and their reality was abundantly demonstrated by critics of Darwin.

Darwin himself fully recognized that natural selection, as he defined it, could not account for all the facts of evolution. Some of his followers, however, usually called *neo-Darwinians* (Weismann was the leading figure), greatly over-emphasized and over-simplified this feature of his theory, and thus brought it into temporary disrepute. The legitimate criticisms of Darwinism, and still more of neo-Darwinism, arose in large part from another and more fundamental imperfection of the theory: lack of knowledge as to how hereditary characters originate and are transmitted. The inadequacies of the Darwinian concept of natural selection and its failures to explain important features of evolution were almost entirely due to erroneous ideas about heredity.

The rise of genetics, the modern science of heredity, is a romantic story and has had an importance for our understanding of life second only to the discovery of the truth of evolution. The story is long and involved and it cannot be told here, but its bearing on evolutionary theory must be explained as briefly as possible. At first, this bearing seemed more confusing than clarifying. An early genetical observation, around the beginning of the century fifty years or so ago, was that hereditary changes arise suddenly and apparently quite at random. With the usual human tendency to over-simplify the complicated, some of the early geneticists (especially de Vries) decided that this was *the* cause of evolution, that evolutionary change takes place in sudden steps and entirely by chance. The abrupt, random changes in heredity observed by the geneticists are called mutations and the attempt to explain evolution on this basis alone is the theory of *mutationism*.

There are random elements in evolution, and these were played up by the mutationists in support of the new theory. Yet it is simply ridiculous to think that evolution occurs entirely at random and, when we look back, it is hard to see how intelligent scientists could ever have thought so, even briefly, as some of them did. The history of the horses shows well enough that there is more than chance and accident in evolution. There is chance, all right, and this is much more evident in some other cases than in the Equidae, but there is also a large and important element that is not chance, that is really anti-chance.

The rise of the modern theory of evolution can be considered as in considerable part a synthesis of chance and anti-chance. The mutationists had discovered and demonstrated an evolutionary factor that appeared to be random: mutation, the sudden rise of new determinants in heredity. Darwin and his followers had discovered and demonstrated an evolutionary factor that is systematic, directional, non-random: natural selection. Put the two together and you have the essential basis for really understanding evolution, although still in greatly over-simplified form.

There is more to heredity than mutation. The genetical contribution to evolutionary theory is much more extensive and subtle than the mere sudden origin of new characteristics. The main basis of heredity is a number of chemical units called genes, thousands of them in each organism, which are strung together in much larger and less numerous groups called chromosomes. A set of these is passed on to the offspring by each parent. In the new individual, the chromosomes and the genes in them determine how development will take place, in reaction, always, to the conditions in which development does occur. Genes interact on each other, and the set as a whole, not each individual gene, determines what will happen as the individual develops. Yet the genes do not blend with each other or get lost. If they did, natural selection would be relatively ineffective, and that was one of the things wrong with the Darwinian theory which postulated blending inheritance.

It is the hereditary differences between individuals that make for evolution. In sexual reproduction (which is usual in the vast majority of both plants and animals), each offspring receives (normally) half its heredity from each parent. This, for a start, means that it will not be exactly like either parent, because in most cases it is impossible that the parents themselves were exactly alike. Then there is also a complicated sort of shuffling of the chromosomes before reproduction occurs, which is practically certain to produce a different set of these in each of the offspring (identical twins, only, excepted). From time to time a sharp change occurs in a gene, or in a chromosome, or in a whole set of chromosomes, producing something distinctly new in the heredity of the resulting offspring. This is a mutation. Mutations occur in only a very small proportion of the population, and yet they do keep on occurring rather steadily and doubtless have since life began.

Sexual reproduction (or rather the shuffling involved in this) and mutation are the processes that produce hereditary variations. They are random, not in the sense that they are uncaused or are due only to haphazard chance, but in the sense that they are not direct responses to the needs of the animal or plant. Their effects, if no other influences were involved, would have no particular relationship to adaptation or even to a possible direction of evolution.

From a genetical point of view, evolution is change in the genetics of successive populations over periods of generations. The changes involve the proportions of given genes and gene sets in the populations and the related spread or the elimination of particular mutations. This leads to a new definition of natural selection which has been developed from Darwin's idea but is essentially different from it and much broader: *natural selection is differential reproduction tending to produce systematic change in the proportions of genes and gene-sets in populations.* If individuals with certain genes or combinations of these tend on an average to have more offspring than others, even if the difference is exceedingly slight, then selection is operating in favor of those genes or combinations. When it is effective, selection determines which mutations are retained, which genes become more common, and which combinations, among untold millions or billions that are possible, will in fact occur. Selection is thus a definitely directional or anti-chance element in evolution. It is also constructive and accounts for the origin of the fit, because it does build up the combinations that determine the character of the organism as a whole. Random elements enter into evolution when genetic shuffling and mutation are predominant over selection. It can also happen that non-adaptive or inadaptive characters can become tied in, within the hereditary and developmental mechanism, with adaptive characters that are being favored by selection.

This is the heart of the mechanism of evolution, the interplay of genetics and selection. Beyond these lie other factors, sometimes of almost incredible complexity. These determine, for instance, just what genes or combinations will in fact be favored by selection, what the relative intensity and effectiveness of selection will be, how this will work out in terms of actual adaptation, what flexibility will exist in the face of changing conditions—and myriads of other actions and reactions as the great history of life sweeps onward. Hence we turn back from the 'why' to the 'how' and see, as has been seen in the history of the horses, how these basic factors of evolution have in fact worked out in particular cases.

It is a peculiarity of any answer to the question 'Why?' that another 'why' always lies beyond it. We reply to conditional or intermediate 'whys,' and never come to the ultimate explanation. Genes, selection, and the multitude of associated factors explain why evolution occurs, but why do these factors operate as they do? Why, in fact, do they exist? Whence came these materials and whence the natural laws under which they live and are molded? Here is the last 'why,' and here the domain of science has been left behind.

APPENDICES

A. WHERE TO SEE FOSSIL HORSES

Complete, mounted skeletons of fossil horses are rarities. They are seldom found, and their preparation is a long, laborious, highly skilled, and expensive job. Much the greater part of the display and research material of fossil horses consists of partial skeletons or, especially, isolated bones, skulls, jaws, and lesser fragments. Of these partial specimens, tens of thousands are known. Of mounted skeletons, there are fifty-odd in the United States (52 are listed below), and some others sufficiently complete to mount have been collected but are not yet assembled. Other mounted skeletons are scattered widely in museums elsewhere in the world, but these probably do not bring the total up to one hundred. As far as I know, there are no mounted skeletons anywhere of *Epihippus, Archaeohippus, Megahippus, Stylohipparion, Nannippus, Calippus, Onohippidium,* or *Parahipparion,* and none in the United States of *Anchitherium* or *Hipparion.* The other eleven established genera of the horse family are represented by mounted skeletons in United States museums, ten of them in a single collection in the American Museum in New York, which has all of these eleven but *Parahippus.*

Almost every natural-history museum throughout the world has some display of fossil horses or of the evolution of the horse. Readers of this book undoubtedly already know their local museums. Here will be listed museums in the United States only. The list is far from complete, but it includes the most important exhibition and research collections and a few of secondary importance scattered widely over the country. Most residents or travelers in the United States will find here some museum they can conveniently visit in order to see specimens of the sort on which the second and third parts of this book are based. Listing is in an approximate geographic sequence, starting in New England and working westward to the Pacific coast. Many of these institutions are still actively collecting fossil horses, so that by the time you visit them their collections may be still more extensive than here indicated on the basis of recent information from officials of the various institutions.

MASSACHUSETTS

Amherst College (Amherst, Massachusetts) has a synoptic exhibit on the evolution of the horse. (This is illustrated in *The Evolution of the Horse* by F. B. Loomis.) There are mounted fossil skeletons of *Hyracotherium, Mesohippus, Merychippus,* and *Equus.* Research collections include representative species from Eocene to Pleistocene, with fair series for the Eocene and the Pliocene (about 60 specimens for each epoch).

In the Museum of Comparative Zoology at Harvard University (Cambridge, Massachusetts) there is an evolution of the horse exhibit with mounted skeletons of *Mesohippus* (two), *Parahippus,* and *Equus* (*Plesippus*). The study collection includes representatives of fifteen genera or subgenera, with especially valuable series for *Mesohippus* (about 85 specimens) and *Parahippus, Merychippus,* and *Neohipparion* (60 to 80 specimens of each).

CONNECTICUT

The Peabody Museum of Natural History at Yale University (New Haven, Connecticut) is of particular interest because in it are preserved the specimens from which Marsh first worked out the essentials of the New World history of the Equidae. There is a synoptic evolution of the horse exhibit and three mounted skeletons are exhibited: *Orohippus, Mesohippus,* and *Equus.* The curator estimates that there are over 2,000 specimens of fossil horses in the study collections, counting isolated limb bones and the like.

NEW YORK

The American Museum of Natural History in New York City has the most complete collections of fossil horses in the world. Some other collections have more individual specimens of some particular form of horse, but none has such extensive, well-rounded representation of all phases of the subject. There are thirteen original and one cast mounted skeletons of fossil horses (twice as many as in any other museum), representing *Hyracotherium* (two skeletons), *Orohippus, Mesohippus* (two), *Miohippus, Merychippus, Hypohippus, Neohipparion, Pliohippus* (two), *Equus* (*Plesippus*), *Equus* (*Equus*), and *Hippidion* (plaster cast of a skeleton in the Argentine Museum in Buenos Aires, mounted here in a new, carefully studied pose). There is also a synoptic panel illustrating evolution of the skull, teeth, and legs with original specimens. Another exhibit includes six mounted skeletons of different recent wild members of the horse family and seven skeletons of domestic horses illustrating extremes of size, important breeds, and phases of action in running, trotting, pulling, etc., along with preparations showing growth, teeth, and other anatomical features. The study collections include thousands of specimens representing almost every known sort of fossil horse. Most modern studies of horse evolution are based in large part on this collection, and it has been a center for preparing and distributing teaching, research, and exhibition materials to many other institutions throughout the world. Affiliated with the American Museum is the Frick Laboratory (not open to the public), which has a superb research collection of middle and later Cenozoic fossil horses.

New Jersey

Princeton University (Princeton, New Jersey) has a synoptic evolution of the horse exhibit and a good series of study specimens, with representative stages throughout the history of the horse but especially good for the early Eocene and the Oligocene. There is a mounted skeleton of *Mesohippus*.

Pennsylvania

The Academy of Natural Sciences of Philadelphia has a synoptic evolution of the horse exhibit but no mounted skeletons. The study series is rather incomplete, with no specimens from the Eocene and few from the Miocene, but has a special interest because it has some of the original specimens studied by the pioneers Leidy and Cope.

The Carnegie Museum (Pittsburgh, Pennsylvania) has a synopotic exhibit and mounted skeletons of *Mesohippus, Merychippus, Equus (Plesippus)*, and *Equus (Equus)*. The study series is good, especially for the Oligocene, but rather weak in Pliocene and Pleistocene forms. There are interesting specimens of early European relatives of the horse, unusual in American museums.

District of Columbia

The United States National Museum has a synoptic exhibit of horse feet and restorations and a fine group of three *Equus (Plesippus)* skeletons. The study collection is among the best, with several thousand specimens representing almost all known stages of horse evolution.

Michigan

The Museum of Paleontology of the University of Michigan (Ann Arbor) has no mounted skeletons of horses and little study material but has a good exhibit on the evolution of the horse.

Illinois

The Chicago Natural History Museum has an outstanding collection in this field. There is a good synoptic exhibit and there are mounted skeletons of *Mesohippus, Pliohippus,* and *Equus (Plesippus)*. There is also a unique habitat group showing life-size restorations of *Mesohippus* in its natural surroundings. The study collection is fairly well rounded, particularly rich in early Eocene horses. Specimens of fossil horses from Central and South America are also of unusual interest.

KANSAS

At the University of Kansas (Lawrence, Kansas) there are an evolution of the horse exhibit and a mounted skeleton of *Mesohippus.* The teaching collection covers the essential stages (14 genera) and there is a large and important research collection representing the later stages (Pliocene and Pleistocene) of the history of horses in the Great Plains region.

NEBRASKA

The State Museum at the University of Nebraska (Lincoln) is potentially another major center for study of horse evolution. A large exhibit includes mounted skeletons of *Mesohippus, Parahippus, Merychippus* (two skeletons), *Neohipparion, Pliohippus,* and *Equus.* There is a rich research collection of several thousand specimens, mostly from the late Tertiary and Pleistocene of Nebraska.

SOUTH DAKOTA

At the School of Mines and Technology (Rapid City, South Dakota) the Museum of Geology has a mounted skeleton of *Mesohippus* and plans to install an exhibit on horse evolution. There is a small study series, mainly from the Oligocene of the South Dakota Big Badlands.

COLORADO

The Colorado Museum of Natural History (Denver) has had a synoptic exhibit on the evolution of the horse, but recently this has been temporarily withdrawn. Three mounted skeletons, still on exhibition, represent Oligocene, Pliocene, and Pleistocene stages. No attempt has been made to develop a research collection.

TEXAS

In Texas there are several collections of fossil horses found in that state, some of them of considerable importance. Among the institutions that have exhibits or study materials are:

West Texas State Teacher's College (Canyon), with one mounted skeleton (*Equus*) and a rich research collection from the late Tertiary and Pleistocene.

Texas Technological College (Lubbock), with an evolution of the horse exhibit but relatively little in the way of research collections.

Texas Agricultural and Mechanical College (College Station), with an evolution of the horse exhibit and some useful local study specimens.

The University of Texas (Austin), also with an evolution of the horse exhibit and some study materials from the late Tertiary and Pleistocene.

CALIFORNIA

The University of California at Berkeley has no mounted skeletons of fossil horses but has a good exhibit on horse evolution (arranged by the late W. D. Matthew, outstanding recent authority in this field) and an adequate study collection, mainly from the later Tertiary and Pleistocene.

The Los Angeles County Museum of History, Science and Art has an attractive and modern synoptic exhibit on this subject, supplemented by two skeletons of *Equus* and one of *Equus* (*Plesippus*). The important Pleistocene remains of *Equus* found in the tar pits of Rancho La Brea are mostly in this museum.

At the California Institute of Technology (Pasadena) there are three mounted skeletons (*Hyracotherium, Neohipparion,* and *Equus*) and a synoptic exhibit. The study collection is rich in specimens from the Pacific coast region, late Oligocene to Pleistocene, and also has an unusual series of specimens from the Pliocene of Mexico.

B. WHERE TO READ MORE ABOUT HORSES

It hardly needs emphasis that much more could be and has been written about every topic touched on in this book. Some readers may want to go on, to browse farther in the rich literature of the horse, to learn more about a particular aspect of this endless subject, or to broaden their general acquaintance with it. An annotated list of some good books for this purpose is given below. All the works cited are in English and most of them are still on the market or widely available in public libraries. Most of the publications listed are non-technical, or near enough so that they can be read with no difficulty after the present volume. A few definitely technical and difficult studies are included, but these are noted as such.

Of course the list is very far from complete, even in regard to popular books. There are literally tens of thousands of publications including discussion of some aspect of the horse family. Here I can only point out a few that appeal to me for one reason or another, and I accept no responsibility if I have left out your favorite horse book. No works of fiction are cited, even though some of these are excellent and informative. I have read all the works listed here, but this is in no sense a citation of 'authorities.' Authorities for the statements in the present book are mainly personal observation and a very large number of technical studies not included in this list.

With one exception (Brown's book on the Arabian horse), I have listed no publications devoted to single breeds of horses. Anyone who wants to learn more about a particular breed should get in touch with the association devoted to registration of that breed. All of these have some literature on their breeds, a leaflet at least, and sometimes large, well-illustrated books. Some of them also publish magazines that keep information on the breed up to date and are full of interesting facts and articles. There are also several magazines devoted to horses in general, and the subject is frequently mentioned in periodicals in the fields of agriculture, country life, and sports. Help in following up some special interest in regard to living American horses can often be obtained from the Horse and Mule Association of America, 407 South Dearborn Street, Chicago 5, Illinois. The U.S. Department of Agriculture and its publications are also

Technical and out of date, but still a basic work on the earliest
horses.

Hogner, D. C. *Our American horse.* Thomas Nelson and Sons, Edinburgh
and New York, 1944.

A simple, good popular summary of ancient and recent horses in
North America.

Huxley, J. *Evolution. The modern synthesis.* Harper and Bros., New
York and London, 1942.

A presentation of the modern synthetic theory of evolution, weak
on fossil evidence and paleontological principles, but otherwise full
and authoritative.

Loomis, F. W. *The evolution of the horse.* Marshall Jones Co., Boston,
1926.

A popular, book-length account, good for its date.

Lull, R. S. *Organic evolution.* 2nd ed. Macmillan, New York, 1932.

Principles of evolution, with a chapter on the horse. A reprint
bears a more recent date, but it is not revised and the discussion of
evolution is now out of date.

ydekker, R. *The horse and its relatives.* George Allen and Co., London,
1912.

Still a valuable account of the anatomy and classification of living
Equidae. The short account of horse ancestry was good when written
ut is now too out of date to be recommended.

tthew, W. D. 'The evolution of the horse.' *Quarterly Review of Biol-
gy,* vol. 1, 1926, pp. 130-85.

Semi-technical, the last word on the subject by the student who
as, until his death in 1930, the greatest authority on horse evolution.

hew, W. D., and S. H. Chubb. 'Evolution of the horse.' *American
useum Guide Leaflet No. 36,* 1913.

Long the best brief, general account of horse ancestry and still use-
(Out of print, but available in many libraries.)

ew, P. O. 'An early Pleistocene (Blancan) fauna from Nebraska.'
d Museum of Natural History, *Geological Series,* vol. 9, no. 2, 1944,
33-66.

ighly technical; important for recent information on the rise of
s and for the author's theory that zebras arose in North America
Equus (Equus) in the Old World.

Thompson, R. F. *The horse.* Edward Arnold, London, 1911.

old but good British book on domestic horses and horsemanship.

R. C. *Introduction to historical geology.* McGraw-Hill, New
1949.

of several good recent books available as geological background
history of the horse, and of all other living things.

e, E. *Animals in motion.* Chapman and Hall, London, 1899.

lassic work on the gaits of the horse, profusely illustrated, and

most helpful. Racing addicts probably need no help in finding th
favorite literature. Identification of specimens and specific informat
on fossil horses can be obtained from natural history museums, som
which are listed in Appendix A.

Besides publications on horses, I have included a few on other
jects mentioned in this book: geology, paleontology, and evolut
have restricted these titles, however, to one or two representative
in each field.

Brown, W. R. *The horse of the desert.* Derrydale Press, 1929.
  Probably the best book on Arabian horses. A less expensiv
  was issued in 1947 by the Macmillan Co., New York.
Camp, C. L., and N. Smith. 'Phylogeny and function of the d
  ments of the horse.' *Memoirs,* Univ. of California, vol. 13,
  pp. 69-124.
  A technical study that has made a profound contributio
  edge of foot structure and its history in horses.
Carter, W. H. 'The story of the horse.' *National Geograp*
  vol. 44, 1923, pp. 455-566.
  With abundant illustrations.
Castle, W. E. 'The ABC of color inheritance in horses.' C
  no. 1, 1948, pp. 22-35.
  At the moment, this is the latest authoritative wo
  and disputed subject. Semi-technical.
Denhardt, R. M. *The horse of the Americas.* Univer
  Press, Norman, 1947.
  A fascinating and authoritative book on the histo
  in both North and South America, and on mod
  States and Latin American horses.
Dinsmore, W., and J. Harvey. *Our equine friends.* I
  ciation of America, 1944.
  An invaluable pamphlet (32 pages), which
  information on domestic horses in America. A
  tions, each of which issues literature on its b
Edinger, Tilly. 'Evolution of the horse brain.' C
  25, 1948.
  Technical; an extremely original and imp
Ellenberger, W., H. Baum, and H. Dittrich.
  of animals for artists. T. Fisher Unwin, L
  A useful classic in the field indicated b
  on the horse.
Flower, W. H. *The horse. A study in natu*
  Co., New York, 1892.
  Old, but still to be read with pleasu
Granger, W. 'A revision of the America
  Mus. Nat. Hist., vol. 24, 1908, pp. 22

still the best work on this subject. 'The horse in motion,' by J. D. B. Stillman, was based on part of the same series of observations and is sometimes cited instead of or in addition to Muybridge as authority on gaits, but Muybridge's book is incomparably better.

Osborn, H. F. 'Equidae of the Oligocene, Miocene, and Pliocene of North America.' *Memoirs Amer. Mus. Nat. Hist.,* new series, vol. 2, part 1, 1918, pp. 1-217.

Still the principal technical compilation on fossil horses of the epochs named. Now rather out of date, and definitely not for the non-professional reader, but a basic work.

Resse, H. H. 'Breeds of light horses.' *U.S. Department of Agriculture, Farmers' Bulletin No. 952, 1918.*

A short, authoritative summary.

Ridgeway, W. *The origin and influence of the Thoroughbred horse.* University Press, Cambridge (England), 1905.

Although many of its conclusions are disputed and the whole subject needs modern restudy, this has long been the standard work on the origin and relationships of domesticated horses in general (and not only of Thoroughbreds).

Riggs, E. S. 'The geological history and evolution of the horse.' *Field Mus. Nat. Hist., Geol. Leaflet No. 13, 1932.*

A short, popular summary.

Romer, E. S. *Vertebrate paleontology.* Revised edition. Chicago University Press, 1945.

An advanced textbook, orienting horse history in that of back-boned animals in general.

Scott, W. B. *A history of land mammals in the western hemisphere.* 2nd ed. Macmillan, New York, 1937.

Semi-popular, richly illustrated account with a good section on horses.

Self, M. C. *The horseman's encyclopedia.* Barnes and Co., New York, 1946.

An invaluable miscellany of information on domestic horses from the point of view of horseman and horselover.

Simpson, G. G. 'Horses and history.' *Natural History,* vol. 38, 1936, pp. 277-89.

Popular account of the domestic horse in the history of mankind.

—— 'How fossils are collected.' *Natural History,* vol. 39, 1937, pp. 329-34.

Not about horses, but explains in pictures and non-technical words how fossil skeletons are collected.

—— 'Resurrection of the dawn-horse.' *Natural History,* vol. 46, 1940, pp. 194-9.

Popular account of the discovery of the oldest known horses.

Simpson, G. G. *The meaning of evolution*. Yale University Press, New Haven, 1949.

   A general account of the broad features of the history of life, of the principles involved in this history, and of the philosophical significance of evolution.

Sisson, S. *The Anatomy of the domestic animals*. 3rd ed., revised by J. D. Grossman. W. B. Saunders Co., Philadelphia, 1938.

   Contains a standard, well-illustrated presentation of horse anatomy.

Stirton, R. A. Phylogeny of North American Equidae. Univ. California Publication, *Bull. Dept. Geol. Sci.*, vol. 25, 1940, pp. 165-98.

   A technical paper by a student of W. D. Matthew, main basis for our present understanding of the lines of horse ancestry.

Stock, C., and H. Howard. 'The ascent of *Equus.*' *Los Angeles County Museum Science Series*, No. 8, 1944.

   A brief, authoritative summary of fossil and living horses.

Tozer, B. *The horse in history*. Methuen and Co., London, 1908.

   A chatty account, with many interesting anecdotes.

Trew, C. G. *From 'Dawn' to 'Eclipse.'* Methuen and Co., London, 1939.

   An interestingly written account of horse history, but the chapters on the evolution of the horse are highly inaccurate.

Vaughan, H. W. *Types and market classes of livestock*. R. G. Adams and Co., Columbus, Ohio, 1919.

   An authoritative discussion of American breeds, except those most recently established.

Vernon, Arthur. *The history and romance of the horse*. Waverly House, Boston, 1939.

   An interesting popular book. A confessedly romantic treatment, the account of prehistoric and early historic horses is often inaccurate.

Vesey-Fitzgerald, B. (editor). *The book of the horse*. Nicholson and Watson, London and Brussels, 1946.

   This book is cited reluctantly because the text, especially in the first hundred-odd pages, contains a great deal of nonsense. The book is, however, beautifully illustrated and some of the later sections include sound information not so readily available elsewhere.

Wyman, Walker D. *The wild horse of the West*. Caxton Printers, Caldwell, Idaho, 1946.

   A conscientious and sympathetic account of our feral horses and Indian ponies, their origin, characteristics, history, and destiny.

INDEX

Figures in italics refer to pages on which there are line-cut illustrations; roman numerals refer to plates.

Academy of Natural Science of Philadelphia, 229
Adaptive radiation, 212-13; of horse relatives, *152*
Africa, wild Equidae, 20 ff.
African rhinoceros, black, 157; white, 157
Age of horse, estimated from teeth, 13-14
Age of Mammals, 99
Age of Man, 99
Albino, color of horses, 72-3, 81-2
Albino A, color of horses, 72, 81; inheritance, 77
Albino B, color of horses, 72
Albino W, color of horses, 72-3, 81, XIII
Allan, 67
Amble, 55-6; broken, 56
American Albino Horse Club, 81
American Museum of Natural History, 91, 228
American Saddle Horse, 66-7, XII; Breeders Association, 67
Amherst College, 228
Amynodontidae, *152*
Analogous structures, 165
Anchitheriinae, classification, 111
Anchitherium, 87, *126*, 128-9, *138*
   classification, 111

Anchitherium (Cont.)
   feet, 197, 203
   place in lineage of Equidae, *114*
   upper molar, *187*
Andalusian horse, 61
Animalia, classification, 4
Ankle, II
Appaloosa, color of horses, 73-4, 80-81, XIII; Horse Club, 81
Arabian horse, 10, *19*, 34 ff., 49, VII
Arabian Horse Club of America, 39
Arabs, 28, VII
Arak, 28
Archaeohippus, 130
   classification, 111
   place in lineage of Equidae, *114*
   upper molar, *187*
Archaeozoic, 98-9
Arikareean, 100
Arm, I
Aryans, 27
Asia, wild Equidae, 17 f.
Asil, 36
Ass, true wild, *19*, 20, IV; Asiatic wild, 18, IV
Assyrian warrior with horse, VI
Astrohippus, *145*
Athens, 31

Back, I
Back tendon, I
Baluchitherium, 157
Barb, 34-5, 61
Barbary, 35

Barstovian, *100*

Barstow, *100*

Bay, color in horses, 71

Beagle, ship, 165

Belgian, 44-5, IX; color, 70

Belly, I

Bering Bridge, *147*

Big Badlands, South Dakota, 124

Bighorn Basin, Wyoming, 116

'Biogenetic law,' 211-12

Black, color of horses, 71; inheritance, 75

Blancan, *100*

Blanco, *100*

Blanco beds, 93

Blood bay, color of horses, 71

Blue roan, color of horses, 73

Blunt, Wilfred and Lady Anne, 38

Bones of horse, II

Bontequagga, *19,* 21, V

Brachydonty, 133

Brain, evolution in Equidae, 176-80; of horse, 8-9

Breast, I

Breed, definition, 42

Breeds, American, 59 ff.; ancient, 34 ff.; European, 42 ff.; origin of, 34 ff.

Bridger, *100*

Bridgerian, *100*

Brisket, I

British Great Horse, 41

British Museum, Natural History, 115

Brontotheriidae, *152*

Brontotherium, XXX

Brown, color of horses, 71

Browsing teeth, *187*

Brule, 100

Bryan, William Jennings, 167

Buckskin dun, color of horses, 72

Buffon, G. L. L. de, 170

Burchell's zebra, *19,* 21

Byerley Turk, 49

Cabrera, Dr. Angel, 59, 61, 148

Calico, color of horses, 73, 80

California Institute of Technology, 231

Calippus, 139, 141; classification, 111; place in lineage of Equidae, *114*

Camp, C. L., 200

Canine tooth, 14

Canon bone, I

Canter, 57

Carnegie Museum, 229

Carpus, II

Castano, color of horses, 59

Castle, W. E., 79, 81

Caudal vertebrae, II

Cavalry horse, VII

Cayuse, 62

Celtic pony, 40, 47, VII

Cement, 15-16, 134, 186, 188

Cenozoic, 98-9

Cerebellar hemispheres, 178

Cerebellum, 178

Cerebral hemispheres, 178

Cervical vertebrae, II

Chadron, *100*

Chadronian, *100*

Chalicotheres, 155-6, XXX

Chalicotheriidae, *152*

Chapman horse, 46

Chestnut, color of horses, 71; inheritance, 77

Chestnut, on leg of horse, I

Chicago Natural History Museum, 229

Chigetai, 18

Chin groove, I

China, appearance of horse in, 25

Chingis, 28

Chromosomes, 223-4

Circus, 30, 32

Citation, 50

Clarendonian, *100*

Class, 4

Cleveland Bay, 46-7, X

Clydesdale, 45-6, IX
Coaltown, 50
Colchester, William, 85
Collecting fossils, XVII
Color, in horses, 69 ff.; of Arabian horses, 37-8; of wild Equidae, 22
Colorado Museum of Natural History, 230
Colorado Rangers, 81
Condylarth, *100*, XIX
Condylarthra, 105 ff.
Conformation, 42
Connemara, 47
Continuity in evolution, 214-15
Convergent evolution, 213-14
Cony, 113
Cooper, Clive Forster, 115
Cope, Edward Drinker, 89, 93, 210, XV
'Cope's law,' 210
Coronado, Francisco Vazquez de, 60
Coronet, I
Cortés, Hernán, 59
Cortex, 178
Cowpony, 40, 60, 62
Coyote, speed, 190
Coyote dun, color in horses, 72
Cream, color in horses, 72; inheritance, 77
Cremello, color of horses, 72
Crest, I
Cretaceous, 100
Criollo, breed, 62, 68
Crotonians, 30
Cummins, W. F., 93
Cuvier, G. L. C. F. D., 153, 155

Darley Arabian, 49
Darwin, Charles, 18, 86, 164-7, 170, 221-3, XVI; Erasmus, 86, 170
Darwinism, 170-71
Dawn horse, *see* Eohippus, 113
Denhardt, R. M., 81

Dentine, 15-16, 134, 186, 188
De Soto, Hernando, 60
Diadiaphorus, XXXII
Diaz del Castillo, Bernal, 59
Diceratherium, XXX
Digit, II
Dinohyus, XXX
Distribution, geographic, 20
Divergence in evolution, 212
Dock, I
Dog, relative speed, 190
'Dollo's law,' 211
Domestication, 24 ff.
Donkey, 20
Dorsal vertebrae, II
Draft horses, definition, 44
Duchesne River, *100, 123*
Duchesnehippus, 123
Duchesnian, *100*
Dun, color of horses, 72

Ear, I
Eclipse, 49; American, 49
Ectoconus, 100
Edinger, Tilly, 176, 179
Edison, T. A., 53
Egypt, ancient horses in, 27
Egyptians, as horse-traders, 34
Elbow, I
Enamel, 15-16, 134, 186, 188
Entelodont, XXX
Eocene, *100;* horses, 113 ff., 120 ff.; length and date of, 102
Eohippus, 24, 89, *100,* 109, 113 ff., *176, 184, 191,* 217, XX, XXXII
  brain, 177-9, *177*
  dentition, 183-4
  feet, 193, *194-6*
  food adaptation, 182
  forearm and shin, *202*
  legs, 201-3
  mounting skeleton, XVIII
  place in lineage of Equidae, *114*
  skull, *175*
  speed, 190

Eohippus (Cont.)
  upper molar, *122*, *187*
  see also Hyracotherium
Epihippus, 100, 121-2, 184
  classification, 111
  place in lineage of Equidae, *114*
  upper molar, *122*, *187*
Equidae, *152*
  ancestry, 103 ff.
  classification, 4, 111
  geographic distribution, 20
  wild, 17 ff., IV, V
Equinae, classification, 111
Equipoise, 50
Equus, 87, 88, *100*, *139*, *143*, *144*,
    159, *176*, *188*, XXXII
  brain, *177*
  classification, 4, 112
  description of, 7 ff.
  feet, *194-6*, 200
  forearm and shin, *202*
  place in lineage of Equidae, *114*
  relative speed, 190
  skeleton in museum, 228, 230,
    231
  skull, *175*
  upper molar, 187
  see also Horse *and names of
    breeds and species*
Equus asinus, *19*, 20, 216, IV
Equus caballus, 17 f., 216; classi-
    fication, 5; races, 26
Equus caballus caballus, *19*
Equus caballus prjewalskii, *19*
Equus (Equus), skeleton in mu-
    seum, 228, 229, XXVIII
Equus grévyi, 19, 22, 216, V
Equus hemionus, 18-21, *19*, 22, 216,
    IV
Equus (Plesippus), skeleton in mu-
    seum, 228, 229, 231, XXVII
Equus quagga, 21, 216-17
Equus quagga burchelli, *19*
Equus quagga granti, V
Equus quagga quagga, V

Equus scotti, XVII
Equus simplicidens, 93-4
Equus stenonis, 145
Equus zebra, *19*, 21-2, 216, V
Evolution, evidence for, 164-9
  explanations of, 218 ff.
  horse brain, 176-80
  horse head, 176-80
  horse limbs and feet, 190-204
  horse skull, 174-6
  horse teeth, 181-9
  patterns, 205 ff.
Extinction of horses in America,
    149-50
Eyes of horse, 9-12, I

Family, 4; nomenclature, 5
Feather, 44
Feet, evolution in Equidae, 190-204
Femur, II
Feral horses, 17, 39
Fetlock joint, I
Fibula, 201-3, II
Finalism, 220-21
Five-gaited horses, 58
Flank, I
Flemish Great Horse, 41, 45; color,
    70
Food, of horse, 15; types of in Equi-
    dae, 181
Forearm, I
Forehead, I
Foretop, I
Fossil horses, hunting and hunters
    of, 85 ff.
Fossilization, 95-6
Fossils, methods of collection, 92-7;
    motives of search for, 163 f.
Fox-trot, gait, 56

Gaits, 52 ff.
Gallop, 56-7, XI, XXXII
Gaskin, I
Genes, 223
Genetics, 222 ff.

Genghis Khan, 28
Genus, 4; nomenclature, 5
Ghor-khar, 18
Godolphin Barb, 49
Grade horses, definition, 43
Granger, Walter, 91
Grant's zebra, V
Gray, color of horses, 73
Grazing horses, rise of, 133-5
Grazing teeth, 187
Great Horse, 40-41, 44, VII
Greece, ancient horses in, 27
Greek horse, VI
Greek horses in art, 30
Gregory, W. K., 144
Grévy's zebra, 19, 22, V
Greyhound, a trotting horse, 63
'Gridiron,' pattern in zebra, 22
Group, I

Hackney, 46, X
Haines, Francis, 60
Ham string, I
Hambletonian, 63
Hand, measure of height, 40
Harness Show Pony, 48
Harrison, 100
Head, evolution in Equidae, 176-80
Hearing, sense of, in horse, 12
Heel, see Hock
Helaletidae, 152
Hemingfordian, 100
Hemphill, 100
Hemphillian, 100
Herod, 49
Hipparion, 87, 88, 138, 138-40, 139
    classification, 111
    feet, 195, 207
    place in lineage of Equidae, 114
    upper molar, 187
Hippeis, 31
Hippidion, 147-8, XXIX
    classification, 111
    skeleton in museum, 228
    skull, 175

Hippotigris, 145
History, horses in, 24 ff.
Hock, 8, II; joint, I
Homologous structures, 165
Hoof, I
Horse, ancient breeds, 34 ff.
    classification, 4-5, 111
    collecting fossil, XVII
    definition, 3 ff.
    desert, 39
    diet, 15
    domestication and human his-
        tory, 24 ff.
    draft, 44
    educated, 9
    false, see Pseudo-horses
    feral, 60
    Flemish, 45
    future, 32
    in ancient art, VI
    intelligence, 8-10
    in warfare, 27-9, 32
    lineage of, 84 ff.
    numbers in United States, 31
    points, I
    Przewalski's, 17 ff., IV
    skeleton, II
    teeth, III
    vision, 9-12
    see also Equus, Equidae, and
        names of breeds, species, and
        genera
Humerus, II
Hunting, on horseback, 30
Huxley, Aldous, 86
Huxley, Julian, 86
Huxley, Thomas Henry, 86, 89,
    XIV; sketch of Eohippus and
    Eohomo, 90
Hyperhippidium, 148
Hypohippus, 88, 126, 129, 138, 185,
    217, XXIII
    classification, 111
    feet, 195, 197
    place in lineage of Equidae, 114

Hypohippus (Cont.)
  skeleton in museum, 228; in rock,
    XVIII
  skull, 175
  upper molar, *187*
Hypsodonty, 133
Hyrachyidae, *152*
Hyracodontidae, *152*
Hyracotheriinae, classification, 111
Hyracotherium, 87, 113 f., 121,
    XIV, XX
  classification, 111
  discovery, 85-6
  place in lineage of Equidae, *114*
  skeleton in museum, 228, 231
  see also Eohippus
Hyracotherium resartum, 121
Hyrax, 113

Iceland pony, 40, VII
Incisor teeth, 13-14, III
India, ancient horses in, 27
Indian pony, 60, 62
Indian rhinoceros, 157
Indians, horses of, 60
Indo-Europeans, 27
Interbreeding, among wild Equi-
    dae, 22
Irreversibility of evolution, 211
Isabel, 38, 71
Isectolophidae, 152
Isolating mechanism, 217

Janus, 65
Javanese rhinoceros, 157
Jaw, I
Jefferson, Thomas, 88
Jennet, 39-40, 61
Jibbah, 38
Jineta, 39-40, 61
Jockey Club, 49

Kalobatippus, 128
Khamsa, el, 37
Khayyam, Omar, 18

Kentucky saddle horse, 66-7
Kiang, 18
Kinetoscope, 53
Kingdom, 4
Klipdass, 113
Knee, I, II
Kovalevsky, Vladimir, 87, XIV
Kudsh, 36
Kuhaylan, 37
Kulan, 18
Kumys, 28

Lamarck, J. B. D. A. de, 170, 219-20
Lead, in gallop and canter, 57
Legs, of horse, proportions, 8
Leidy, Joseph, 88, XIV
Lemuroids, 24
Libyans, 34
Limbs and feet, evolution in Equi-
    dae, 190-204
Lincoln, Abraham, 170
Linnaean hierarchy, 4
Liver chestnut, color of horses, 71
Loins, I
Lope, 58
Lophiodontidae, *152*
Los Angeles County Museum of
    History, Science, and Art, 231
Lumbar vertebrae, II

Mahogany bay, color in horses, 71
Mammalia, classification, 4
Man, association with horse, 24; re-
    lationship with horses, 104
Mandible, II
Mane, I
'Mark,' on horse incisors, 13
Marsh, Othniel Charles, 89, 113,
    XV; genealogy of the horse, 90
Marx, Groucho and Harpo, 167
Matchem, 49
Matthew, William Diller, 91, 92,
    123, XVI
McGrew, P. O., 145

Megahippus, 129, *138,* 185; classification, 111; place in lineage of Equidae, *114*

Merychippus, 88, 100, *126, 134,* 131 ff., *137-8, 139, 144,* 185, 215, XXIV
brain, *177,* 180
classification, 111
dentition, 186-9
feet, *194-6,* 197-200, 204, 207
forearm and shin, *202*
place in lineage of Equidae, *114*
skeleton in museum, 228, 229, 230
skull, *175*
upper molar, *187*

Mesohippus, 88, 100, 124-6, *126,* 185, XXXII
brain, *177,* 179
classification, 111
feet, *194-6,* 197
forearm and shin, *202*
legs, 203
place in lineage of Equidae, *114*
skeleton in museum, 228, 229, 230
skull, *175*
upper molar, *187*

Mesopotamia, appearance of horse in, 25
Mesozoic, 98-9
Messenger, 63
Mesteño, 61
Metacarpal, II
Metatarsal, II
Mexico, conquest of, 59
Migrations of horses, 128, 140, 145-7
Milk teeth, 13-14
Miocene, *100;* horses, 127 ff., 131 ff.; length and date of, 102

Miohippus, 100, 126, 127, *127, 134,* XXI
classification, 111
place in lineage of Equidae, *114*
skeleton in museum, 228
Mitbah, 38

Mohammed, 69
Mohammedan, 28
Molarization of horse premolars, *184*
Molars, 14 ff.
Mongols, 28-9
Morgan, Justin, 64
Morgan, breed, 64-5, XII
Moropus, XXX
Motion pictures, invention of, 52 ff.
Mountain zebra, *19,* 21-2, V
Mouse dun, color in horses, 72
Mule, 22
Muscles, 8
Mustang, 40, 60-62, 74; The Phantom, 69
Mutation, 223-5
Mutationism, 223
Muybridge, Eadweard, 52-4, 163, XI
Muzzle, I

Nannippus, 138-40, 188
classification, 111
place in lineage of Equidae, *114*
upper molar, *187*
Nannippus phlegon, 140
Names, technical, 110
Natural selection, 221-2, 224-5
Near East, ancient horses in, 26
Neck, I
Neo-Darwinism, 222
Neohipparion, 138-40, *138, 139,* XXV
classification, 111
place in lineage of Equidae, *114*
skeleton in museum, 228, 230, 231
skull, *175*
upper molar, *187*
Neo-Lamarckism, 219-20
Nez Percé Indians, 81
Nomenclature, zoological, 4-5
Nose, I
Nostril, I
Notohippidae, 158
Notohippids, 213-14

Numidian horses, 34
Numidians, 34

Old Stone Age paintings of horse,
    VI
Olfactory bulbs, 178
Oligocene, *100;* horses, 124 ff.;
    length and date of, 102
Olympia, racing at, 30
Onager, 18, *19*
Onohippidium, 148; classification,
    111
Order, 4
Orellan, 100
Organism, 172
Orientation in evolution, 207-8
Orohippus, 100, 121-2, *184,* XXI
    classification, 111
    place in lineage of Equidae, *114*
    skeleton in museum, 228
    upper molar, *122*
Orthogenesis, 205-6
Osorn, Henry Fairfield, 91, XV
Overo, color of horses, 73, 80
Owen, Richard, 86, 113

Pace, 56; stepping, 56
Pachynolophus, 120, 151
Pad-foot, in earl horses, 193-8
Paint, color of horses, 73
Palaeotheres, 120
Palaeotheriidae, 151, 152
Palaeotherium, 87, 151-4
Paleocene, *100;* length and date of,
    102
Paleocene-Eocene transition, 115-16
Paleozoic, 98-9
Palomino, 38, 74-5, XIII
    color in horses, 71-2; inheritance,
        of, 77-9
    Horse Association, 74
    Horse Breeders of America, 75
Paloplotherium, 154
Panama Bridge, *147*

Parahipparion, 148; classification,
    112
Parahippus, 88, *100, 126, 131* ff.,
    185, 215
    classification, 111
    dentition, 186-7
    place in lineage of Equidae, *114*
    skeleton in museum, 228, 230
    upper molar, *187*
Parallel evolution, 213-14
Paramedian lobes, 178
Parthenon, 30
Parti-colored, color of horses, 73
Parts of horse, *see* Points
Pastern, I
Peabody Museum of Natural His-
    tory, Yale University, 228
Pelvis, II
Percheron, 44-5, IX; color, 69
Perissodactyla, *152,* 154; classifica-
    tion, 4
Phalanx, II
Phenacodus, 105 ff., 109, XIX
Phyletic evolution, 216-17
Phylum, 4
Piebald, color of horses, 73
Pied, color of horses, 73
Pinto, color of horses, 73, 80, XIII;
    Horse Society, 80
Pisiform bone, I
Plagiolophus, 154, 213-14
Plantation Walker, 67
Pleistocene, *100;* horses, 145 ff.;
    length and date of, 102
Pliny, 30
Pliocene, *100;* horses, 129, 137 ff.,
    142 ff.; length and date of, 102
Pliohippus, 100, 139, 142, 144, 215,
    XXVI
    brain, *177*
    classification, 111
    feet, *195-6,* 204, 207
    place in lineage of Equidae, *114*
    skeleton in museum, 228, 230
    skull, *175*

Pliohippus (Cont.)
    upper molar, *187*
Poictiers, battle, 28
Point, of buttock, I; of hip, I; of
    hock, I; of shoulder, I
Points of horse, I
Poll, I
Polo, 68
Ponies, 47-8
Pony, Celtic, 40; Indian, 40; polo,
    67
Premolars, 14 ff.
Princeton University, 91, 229
Propachynolophus, 120
Proterotheres, 213-14
Proterotheriidae, 159-60
Proterozoic, 98-9
Protohippus, 137, *139, 144;* upper
    molar, *187*
Przewalski's horse, 17 f., *19,* IV
Pseudo-albino, color of horses, 72,
    81
Pseudo-horses, 157-60, *159,* XXXII
Puercan, *100*
Punch, Suffolk, 46
Pupil, of horse's eye, 11
Purebred, definition, 43

Quagga, 21, V
Quantum evolution, 216-17
Quarter Horse, 65-6, XII

Races, chariot, 30; Greek and Ro-
    man, 30
Racing, harness, 63
Rack, 55-6
Radioactivity, geologic dating by,
    101
Radius, 201-3, II
Randomness in evolution, 206-8
Rate of evolution, 214
Recapitulation, principle of, 211-12
Recent (times), *100;* length and
    date of, 102
Red roan, color of horses, 73

Registration of breeds, 42-3
Rhinoceros, 156-7, XXX, XXXI
Rhinocerotidae, *152*
Ribs, I, II
Richardson, William, 85
Roan, color of horses, 73
Rochon-Duvigneaud, A., 10
Rodeos, 32

Sacral vetebrae, II
Saddle Horse, 66-7
Saddler, 33, 66-7
Saltation, 214-15
San Juan Basin, New Mexico, 116
Sandy bay, color in horses, 71
Scapula, II
School of Mines and Technology,
    South Dakota, 230
Scott, William Berryman, 91, 148,
    XVI
Selection in evolution, *see* Natural
    selection
Sesamoid, II
Sexual reproduction, 224
Shakespeare, William, 39
Shank, I
Sheep Creek, *100*
Shetland pony, 47-8
Shetlands, 45
Shilo, 66
Shire, 45
Single-foot, 56
Sires, foundation, of American Sad-
    dle Horse, 67
    Tennessee Walking Horse, 67
    Thoroughbred, 49
Skeleton of horse, II
Skewbald, color of horses, 73
Skull, II
Skull, *Equus,* 12, *12;* evolution in
    Equidae, 174-6
Smell, sense of, in horse, 12
Smith, N., 200
Solutré, Stone Age horse at, 24
Sorrel, color of horses, 71

South America, false horses, 158; fossil horses, 146-8
Spain, 39; ancient horses in, 27
Spanish horses, types introduced in America, 61
Specialization in evolution, 208-10
Speciation, 215-17
Species, 4; nomenclature, 5
Speed, adaptation for, 8; of horses, 50-51
Splint bone, II
Spring-foot, in later horses, *196*, 198-200
Staked Plains, 92
Standard Bred, 63-4, XII
Stanford, Leland, 52-3, 163
Steel Dust, 66
Stifle joint, I
Stillman, J. D. B., 53
Stone Age horses, 24
Strawberry roan, color of horses, 73
Stud book, 43
Stylohipparion, 140; classification, 111; place in lineage of Equidae, *114*
Suffolk, 45-6, IX; color, 69
Sumatran rhinoceros, 157
Survival of the less-specialized, 210
Sybarites, dancing horses, 30

Tail, I
Tapiridae, *152*
Tapirs, 156, XXXI
'Tarpans,' 17
Tarsus, II
Teeth, 12 ff.
   Equus, 12, *12*
   evolution in Equidae, 181-9
   grinding or cheek, 14
   of domestic horse, III
Tennessee Walking Horse, 67-8, XII
Tertiary, 101
Texas Agricultural and Mechanical College, 230

Texas Panhandle, 92
Texas Technological College, 230
Thigh, I
Thoatherium, 159
Thomson, Albert, 91
Thoroughbred, 33, 39, 48-51, X, XI
Three-gaited horses, 58
Throat, I
Thompson, C. and R., 81
Tibia, 201-3, II
Tiffanian, *100*
Tiffany, *100*
Time, geologic scale, 98 ff.
Titanotheres, *152*, 155, XXX
Tobiano, color of horses, 73, 80
Torrejon, *100*
Torrejonian, *100*
Transformation in evolution, 208
Trend evolution, 208
Trot, 56
Trotting horse, 63-5
Type of horses, definition, 42

Uinta, *100*
Uintan, *100*
Ulna, 201-3, II
United States National Museum, 229
University of California, 231
University of Kansas, 230
University of Nebraska, 230
University of Texas, 230

Valentine, 100
Vaqueros, 60
Vermis, 178
Vertebrae, II; numbers of, in horses, 38
Vestigial structures, 165
Vision, of horse, 9-12
Vitalism, 220-21

Walk, gait, 54-5; running, 55-6
Walking Horse, 67-8
Warfare, horses in, 27-9, 32

Wasatchian, *100*
Weismann, F. L. A., 222
Welsh pony, 47-8, X
Wentworth, Lady, 39
West Texas State Teacher's College, 230
Whippet, *191*
White, color of horses, 72-3, 81-2
White Horse Ranch, 81
Whitney, 163
Whitneyan, *100*

Wild horses, 17
Willwood, *100*
Withers, I
'Wolf tooth,' 14
Wrist, II

Yale University, 89
Ysabella, 71

Zebra, *19*, 21 ff., V
Zoopraxiscope, 53

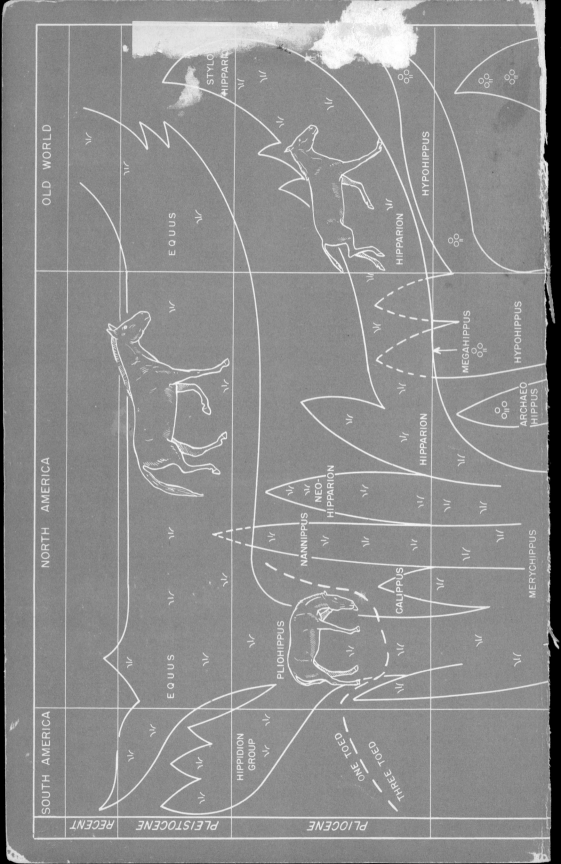